A *Home for*
MERLIN

A Home for MERLIN

Sheila Jeffries

WELBECK

Published in 2021 by Welbeck Fiction Limited,
part of Welbeck Publishing Group,
20 Mortimer Street London W1T 3JW

Cover design by Alexandra Allden
Cover photograph © Shutterstock.com

The quote on page 280 is from the hymn *Great is Thy Faithfulness*:
'Summer and winter, and spring time and harvest.'

A CIP catalogue record for this book is available from the British Library

Paperback ISBN: 978-1-78739-575-6
E-book ISBN: 978-1-78739-576-3

Printed and bound by CPI Group (UK) Ltd., Croydon, CR0 4YY

10 9 8 7 6 5 4 3 2 1

To Pete and Rosie

Chapter 1

A Broken Heart

'Out you go, cat.'

A pair of bony hands grabbed me and dumped me outside. Raindrops glistened on the doormat, soaking my soft golden paws as I turned to look reproachfully at the woman who had evicted me. Didn't she know I had a broken heart and was desperate for a home? Didn't she care?

She didn't. The door slammed in my face. I could still smell the toast and coffee aroma of the bright interior. It was a cold December night and the heat of a log fire was something I craved.

It wasn't the first time I'd been chucked out that day. I'd been following a group of fundraisers who were knocking on doors, rattling their red collecting tins, giving out stickers and talking in cheerful voices. They wore warm coats, boots and scarves. 'Thank

1

you very much. Thank you,' they said as the donated coins jingled into the tin. Then a conversation would start and a door would be open – my chance to slip inside and head for the cosy fire. My fur was wet from the rain, and each time I was thrown out the ache in my ribs deepened, and loneliness throbbed in my veins.

I was a ginger cat. A NICE ginger cat.

And nobody wanted me.

I'd lost my beloved human, Imelda. It wasn't her fault, or mine. For weeks and weeks, I'd been searching for her, living wild, running miles across country. I was only a young cat, and tonight I felt old and thin, my paws were sore, my lovely ginger fur harsh and matted. Cold wind and driving rain had made me seek shelter in this village by the sea, and the cheerful group of fundraisers had given me hope.

I charged after them as they plodded on up the street. I mustn't lose them.

'Here he is – still following us.' A man with white hair, who the others called Theo, kept looking down at me, a glint of kindness in his eyes. He stooped to stroke me and I arched my back, appreciating his touch and the homely smell of his overcoat. This might be my only hope of finding a fireside. I trotted after him with my tail up.

Cats don't give up, I told myself. A cat never gives up, not even one with a broken heart.

I pressed myself against Theo's legs and purred. He seemed frail but his voice had a special resonance that sent tiny bubbles of pleasure coursing through me.

Again I waited for the next cottage door to open and, when it did, I shot in. Oh, the bliss! Inside was a massive iron stove and a woolly hearthrug, exactly right for a cat. I kneaded its sumptuous pile with my front paws, turning around slowly, preparing to flop down and stretch out in the delicious heat. My bones ached with the cold. I was tired, very tired, and hungry too.

In a chair by the fire was a newspaper with legs. It didn't notice me so I focused on the glorious heat from the dancing flames.

For a few moments, I luxuriated in the warmth, listening to the clunk of coins and Theo's low-pitched voice. 'Thank you, my dear. And I hope you have a pleasant evening.'

'Goodnight, Theo,' she called and closed the door. I heard her brisk feet tapping through the hall, and then a scream. 'A CAT! Get it out of here. You know I hate cats. Wake up, you useless lump, hiding behind yer newspaper as usual.'

I rolled over and tried to appear harmless and friendly.

'Get rid of it, Percy.'

A startled face emerged from behind a newspaper and studied me with guarded wonder. Obviously, Percy loved cats. He wanted to touch me. But before he could even stretch out a hand, SHE snatched his newspaper and rolled it furiously into a baton. I knew exactly what a folded newspaper meant to a cat so I moved fast, my claws ripping threads from the rug. I fled to the front door and scrabbled at it, meowing piteously, praying she would open it before she swiped me.

'Don't hit the poor devil,' the man called as she flung open the door. Devil? Me? I burst out of the house and fled into the night. I'd had enough. That lovely fire. A haze of warmth lingered on the tips of my coat but it hadn't had time to seep through my dense ruff of fur. Hunger growled in my belly and I slowed to a trot. I thought of happiness and the fun I used to have. I felt miserable now. Starving and unwanted.

The fundraisers were crowding into the pub further down the road. There was laughter and the clink of glasses. I shivered as they disappeared inside. The night was bitterly cold and I hadn't got a bed.

'Come on, puss.' A voice – calling me! Theo was outside, by himself, sitting on a bench. I ran to him, meowing. 'Lost, are you?' he asked as I gazed into his eyes. 'That makes two of us.' Theo was eating an enormous Cornish pasty wrapped in crackly paper. It steamed in the cold air and flakes of pastry were getting caught in his silver beard. 'You want a bit, do you, puss?'

I meowed, and he broke off a chunk of pasty and put it on the ground for me. It had ragged cubes of peppery meat inside. I ate every bit except the lumps of tangy turnip, which I disliked. The heat of it in my tummy felt good.

'So you like Cornish pasties, puss?' I meowed for more and he gave me another piece. When we'd both finished, I sat looking up into the glint of his eyes.

'That makes two of us,' Theo said, again, and I sensed the meaning of his words. He slowly added more. 'Lonely . . . and unwanted.'

I gazed, and began to purr deeply, knowing how it comforted humans. Theo stooped and picked me up. He unbuttoned his coat and held me against his heart. It was beating steadily and I could hear a watch ticking in his waistcoat pocket. He wasn't who I would have chosen . . . but he would have to do. Clearly, he needed a cat, and not just any old cat. Theo needed me.

'Where do you live then, puss?' He fiddled with my collar. 'You've lost the medallion, haven't you?'

I leaned against him, feeling his breath in my fur as he slid the collar round. I remembered Imelda taking my collar off one day and writing my name along it with a sparkly pen. Was it still there? I hoped Theo would read it to me, and he did.

'M . . . E . . . R . . .' He paused, and his old eyes twinkled with forgotten fire. 'MERLIN!' A change came over him, a kind of light, like late afternoon sunlight flooding a garden and turning the twigs golden. 'Merlin,' he said again. 'It can't be! But strange things do happen, here in Tintagel.'

I was so pleased to hear my name. The sound of it awakened my own special light. We studied each other under the glow of a lantern above us on the wall. I began to notice things that sparkled in the night. The stars, high up and distant. The glow from cottage windows. I knew I was meant to be with Imelda. She loved me, and I'd helped her a lot just by listening and purring, and by sitting with her and waiting for her to calm down when she was upset.

But perhaps Theo would give me a home, just for now.

Theo was quiet for an expanded moment, as if he were deep under water, in the dark of his darkest thoughts.

I waited, purring.

'Merlin,' he said at last, in a respectful whisper. 'A cat called Merlin. You've been sent to me. I've got a little place, with a cosy fire. Come home with me, Merlin. Come home.' He patted his shoulder and I climbed up there, and purred in his ear.

It was good to be carried again, to cling on and feel his warmth under the thick jacket. Good to experience the rhythm of footsteps carrying me like a boat over waves. I looked around with interest, studying the night sky, like cats do. At the edge of the village were cliffs with black, mysterious rocks and the phosphorescence of the sea.

Theo's place seemed a long way out of the village. With me on his shoulder he plodded down towards the sea, along a rocky path, the beam of his torch illuminating a wall built from sharp slates, encrusted with tough little cushions of plant life. Beyond the wall the land dipped steeply into a chasm darker than midnight. I could hear waves a long way down, sucking and splashing, and the high-frequency song of dolphins far out on the night sea. Dolphins were creatures I found interesting. I longed to sit there, on my own, in the morning sun, and communicate with them. Being a cat is brilliant, for we cats have heightened awareness and sensitivity that few humans can match or even imagine. Especially in a place like Tintagel, where the rocks and the cottage walls are storehouses of legends and stories. I could sense them, more and more, as we approached Theo's home.

'Nearly there, Merlin.' He reached up and stroked my chin with his chunky thumb. He took a huge iron key from his pocket. 'My little cave,' he said happily and shone the torch over an extraordinary cottage, built into the cliff face. I saw tiny diamond windows and a hanging mass of creeper. Clusters of icicles glinted in its tangle of branches but even in the depths of winter the creeper bristled with hibernating life: ladybirds, moths, wild bees and sleeping sparrows; goldcrests and wrens huddling together in tightly woven nests. Around the front door the walls glittered with crystals. I had come to a place where even the stones were alive. My fur began to prickle. I slid down from Theo's shoulder and sat close to his feet. A new home. A cosy chair. A safe place to sleep. I couldn't wait.

But seconds later we were inside that ancient oak door and I was desperate to get out. I glimpsed the embers of a fire and two chairs. A bookshelf. I heard Theo's concerned voice. 'What's the matter, Merlin? There's nothing to be scared of.'

How could I tell him? I wailed and scrabbled. My eyes must have gone black with terror. I couldn't possibly stay in there. I wailed and cried and, with a sigh of disappointment, Theo let me out and I vanished into the night.

Chapter 2

Imelda's Kitten

It was the way their eyes gleamed and glittered in the firelight. A line of fierce cats on a high shelf in Theo's living room, glaring down at me!

Naturally wary, I had spotted them before Theo managed to shut the door. Imagine being trapped in there – with them! I knew how to fight. How to bush out my fur, flatten my ears and make bloodcurdling yowls in the back of my throat. My claws were sharp, and fast, and accurate. So why was I afraid?

Upset and shaken, I scrambled up a small yew tree, the night air chilling my fur. Safe in the dense greenery, I clung to a branch, peering out between clusters of leaves.

Theo stood in the doorway in a shaft of light, calling me. 'Merlin? Come on. Come on . . . it's warm in here.' He clicked his fingers. 'I thought we were friends.' I didn't move. Surely he couldn't see me hidden in the tree.

'Come on. Puss, puss.' He tried whistling. Then he disappeared inside and came out with a food bowl. He stood there tapping it. He lowered his voice to a whispery squeak. 'Kitty, kitty.'

My nose twitched. Fish. I could smell fish. Yum. But I wasn't going to move. Was it my destiny to be alone and hungry? Why were those terrible cats in there, in what might have been my new home? I stared, my neck stretched out, my whiskers tense, my heart beating furiously as I tried to see those cat faces inside. They'd been high up, on a shelf, and I couldn't see them now. I wanted Theo. I trusted him. Why didn't he come out and sit in the yew tree with me? Disappointed, I watched the calling and dish-tapping become less and less hopeful, and, predictably, he turned and went back inside. I stared at the firmly closed door. Moonlight glinted on its two whorls of thick glass and on the brass knocker, which was shaped like a lion's head.

Then I saw something that made me sit up very straight. A cat flap! In the lower panel of the door. I could get in . . . or those bone-chilling cats could get out. I listened attentively. The trouble with cat flaps is that you never know who or what is going to come out, or come in.

I focused on it. Was it moving? I imagined a cat with angry eyes. It would know exactly where I was hiding.

I tensed as the main door swung open, but Theo was there again, in his slippers, without his hat, his tufts of hair silver in the lamplight. He was clutching one of those cats. Its eyes gleamed. It was rigid, like a dead cat. My fur began to prickle.

'Come on, Merlin. I know you're out there,' Theo called, 'and I know what you're scared of: my cats. There're not real. I brought one out to show you. It's china.' He tapped it with a coin and made a chinking sound. He put the stiff cat on the doorstep and gave it a push. It fell over sideways and lay deathly still, the moonlight pooled in its porcelain eyes. Not a twitch or a flicker of movement.

I was spooked. My tail had expanded to twice its usual size. I couldn't take my eyes off the motionless body of the china cat. Theo was looking down at it as if he hoped it might come to life. With my intuition on alert, I sensed this 'cat' had no heat and no energy. It was cold, cold, cold. It was a nothing cat.

With that revelation, my fur subsided and I began to feel foolish. I'm a sensitive cat and my brilliantly clear eyesight plays tricks on me. I'd been the same with Imelda's collection of teddy bears. Spooked. Until I realised they were inanimate lumps of fluff, and I got fierce with them, beating them up, even dragging them into the bathroom, or rolling them down the stairs. My tail twitched with glee at the memory.

Ashamed of my mistake, I called to Theo with a loud meow, and jumped nonchalantly out of the yew tree, my tail like a tall ship's mast, my fur flouncing as I trotted over to him.

'Aw, there you are. Lovely boy.' He looked pleased, and I was glad to be welcomed. Disregarding the china cat on the floor, I rubbed my head against Theo's legs. 'Are you coming in now?' he asked. He wasn't going to force me. Trust is a soothing flow of warmth to body and soul, and I basked in it. I ran to the hearth-rug. The flames were luminous. They danced for me, twisting and weaving, orange with sudden spurts of blue.

After long hours of cold, the heat was already reaching my bones. What bliss! I purred and kneaded the thick woolly rug with my front paws. Theo sat watching me, his hands wrapped around a chunky blue-and-white mug. 'You've got really big paws,' he remarked. 'Broad and powerful. Like a Shire horse.' He grinned. I didn't know what a Shire horse was, but it sounded good. I was proud of my golden paws. They were soft and strong.

I love it when humans smile at me. Aware of my power to coax a smile from Theo's rather serious face, I made a decision to behave nicely. With Imelda, I'd been a mad, tearaway kitten. That had to change. This was an old man's cottage – polished wood, dark-red rugs, copper kettles and shelves of books. Later, I'd show Theo how I was able to pull down a book with my paw and open it, but I wouldn't tear the pages. Books were important to humans. Books were mysterious and interesting. Imelda used to read me stories and I enjoyed looking at the pictures and trying to figure out what they were supposed to be.

I followed my nose and strolled through another door into the kitchen, and devoured the tuna Theo had put down for me. When I'd had enough, I sniffed the earthenware dish again. Another cat had used it. Then I discovered a cosy cat bed in a corner and found the same familiar scent on it, with traces of fur. Theo saw the question in my eyes. 'That was my Josephine's bed.' His old eyes filled with grief. 'She's gone. My daughter, Sarah, took her away. She was a lovely little cat.' He picked me up and carried me back to the fireside chair. 'She was a sweetie. Light as air, she was – I could pick her up with one hand – and so pretty, silver-grey and white, with big, expressive eyes, like a frost fairy.'

I listened, intrigued by the passion in his voice. He tapped a photo frame, which was on the table beside his chair. 'Here she is, see, my Josephine.' I stared at a picture of a wispy, whimsical cat. A spark of surprise went through me. I couldn't understand how she could be there, in a flat square of glass.

Theo seemed to know my mind. 'I've lost her, Merlin,' he confided, 'but you're here now, and you are marvellous. You're a golden cat. Like the Sun King.' He nodded and sat down with me on his lap. 'I hope you'll stay with me, Merlin – even if Josephine does come back. This is your home.'

I gave a deep sigh. If only I could explain how much it meant to me. I sent him the thought and, after a moment of quiet, he said, 'You've been a stray for too long, Merlin, haven't you?'

I wanted to respond but drowsiness overwhelmed me. At last I could sleep. A home. I'd found a home.

I stretched out over Theo's warm body and allowed myself to purr, sending the vibration into his heart. A sad old heart, like a tulip with only one petal left. I gazed up at him and caught the sparkle of a teardrop on his cheek.

'Dear cat,' he murmured, and we touched noses, bonding for ever. I relaxed into a new wave of purring, loving the touch of his hand caressing my back.

He went on and on smoothing me and I felt my coat recovering from being harsh and bristly in the cold. The rhythmic stroking was turning my ginger fur to silk.

We fell asleep together in the chair with the fire burning down into crimson caverns and snowy white flakes of ash. Outside, the night moved on, sighing with the roar of waves foaming against cliffs. Inside, a clock ticked and the wind sang through a crack in the door.

Safe. I am safe, I thought, and remembered the bliss of being a glossy-furred lap cat. Theo's cat. *But not for ever.* Theo wanted to keep me. I'd stay through the dark days of winter. But how could I tell him I was on a journey? An impossible journey to find Imelda.

Imelda was my priority. It was my job to help her.

My life as an earth cat was getting complicated.

* * *

Once I was a shining cat living in the spirit world between lifetimes.

I lived there in a beautiful garden full of light. The leaves and petals sparkled like diamonds, the way they do on earth after a rainstorm. Roses spilled down from great cathedrals of growth, long tassels of wisteria blossom intertwined with white-and-purple passion flowers. Moss and silken grasses cushioned the ground. Fragrance drifted through the blue air and sometimes music from tubular bells and wind harps.

I loved it there in that blessed garden of peace. I could rest and dream and play if I wanted to, and sleep under the wing of an angel. The wing shimmered over me like a sky with clouds of pearl, an endless protective shell with secret rainbows. Learning to see them fascinated me, kept me still, and taught me skills that would help me survive another earth-life.

The best thing I learned was the power of stillness. Keeping still made me a better cat than when I was charging around. Stillness brought me wisdom, energy and confidence. It wasn't boring. It was intensely interesting because I noticed astonishing details I might otherwise have missed. I listened to higher frequency sounds, like the language of dolphins and the hidden music of plants. Even the sun, moon and stars sang to me when I was quiet and still. That's how I learned to hear the voices of angels.

Beyond the garden stretched the shining lands, an ethereal world of misty mountains, green valleys and cloud-capped palaces, but I had no desire to explore it. I was a contented cat spirit.

But one morning the angel's wing began to move, slowly at first, then faster, with a sense of urgency until I could see the gold-rimmed edge of it, exposing the sky and the distant mountains. I tingled with excitement. I'd never seen the whole angel but now I did, and I gazed up at her in awe. She was like a pillar of light, so dazzlingly bright that I couldn't see her face.

I listened. The wind hummed in the tamarisk trees and brought me her voice. 'We need you, Merlin, for another earth-life. A girl, Imelda, needs you. She is having a difficult time at school with bullies and is having trouble coping with her father's behaviour at home. Will you go?'

Would I go? Of course I would. I was already stretching my shining fur into the light, my tail held lofty and exuberant. Happy to be chosen, I turned my emerald eyes to the angel, knowing she would see that I was willing.

'It won't be easy,' she warned, 'but you are a strong spirit, Merlin, and you understand the language of humans well.'

I did a purr-meow, which is a cat's most spiritual greeting.

'I will always be close,' the angel assured me. 'You have only to remember the canopy of my wing and listen to my voice. In the midst of all the human voices, mine will be the one that comes to you on the wind.'

I moved around the hem of her skirt, in and out of tiny curls and ruffles of light. She picked me up. 'Let us go.'

In a whoosh of sparkles, the angel carried me out of the garden, through the woods and the mountains, until we came to a river. I stared in surprise at the colours of its slow-flowing waters – shades of indigo, violet and kingfisher blue weaving together with pine-forest greens and the blackest of blacks.

'This is the River of Forgetfulness,' the angel explained. 'Every soul who is to be born on earth must cross it. It induces a temporary state of amnesia so that you can be born with a clear and happy mind.'

The angel held me tightly. 'In a moment I shall let you go, Merlin, and you will glide across the River of Forgetfulness as if in a dream. You will wake up in the body of a ginger kitten who has just been born. Your mum cat has waited a long time for you, and she loves you. Listen as I let you go, and you will hear her purring.'

It happened exactly as the angel predicted. She let me go, and I slipped into a dreamless sleep. My next sensation was of being licked by the gigantic tongue of my mum cat – no, I realised, her tongue wasn't gigantic, but I was incredibly small. I felt her breath and her stiff whiskers. Her purring went right through me like the buzz of a bumblebee. I longed to see her eyes, but mine were not yet open. I flexed my perfect little paws and felt my way along her furry body where I suckled blissfully, tasting her sweet milk. There were others alongside me, other tiny kittens squirming with joy inside the cosy nest of purring.

I had arrived safely.

Born with a clear and happy mind.

On the ninth day, my eyes opened and I saw my front paws. The fur was gloriously ginger with bands of light, honey-gold. I was the only ginger kitten. The others were tabby-and-white, and tortoiseshell. I had four siblings, with bright blue eyes in cute little faces. And at last I saw my mum cat's eyes, alert and wise, but glistening with love for me. I wanted to stay with her for ever, for all of my life.

But it was not to be.

When I was eight weeks old, a family came to our home to choose a kitten. *Please don't let it be me,* I prayed. I snuggled close to my mum cat and she put her long front paw right over me. I pretended to be asleep but I was listening – and peeping.

My brothers and sisters were walking about, squeaking with their tails up as if they wanted to be chosen. A woman with a loud, ringing voice seemed to be in charge of the family. She had cold, dispassionate eyes. The man, Brad, wasn't interested in us kittens but peered all around the room, fidgeting. 'You've got a patch of damp in that corner,' he said to my mum cat's human. 'I could fix that for you if—'

'Brad!' His wife looked at him sharply. 'Kittens.'

'Yeah, OK, Chloe.'

Brad picked up one of my tabby sisters. Instead of cuddling her, he held her up in the air with her little legs dangling. 'This is a pretty one, Imelda.'

There was a teenage girl next to him with sorrowful brown eyes. Imelda! The name chimed in my heart. She shook her head. 'But, Dad, I want a ginger one. You never listen.'

'Don't be rude, or you won't have one at all,' Chloe snapped.

'I wasn't.'

'Yes, you WERE.'

'Anyway, I want a ginger kitten.'

Brad put my sister down. She stood there, bewildered, her tail down. Our mum cat called her in with a purr-meow, and started to wash her with loving care.

I peeped out at Imelda, and I felt drawn to her. She needed a cat – in fact, she needed me. I wanted to go and help her. She had such sad eyes. But I wasn't ready to leave my mum cat.

Then Chloe gasped. My heart sank as I met those cold eyes. She'd seen me! 'Oh,' she crowed, 'here's a ginger one.'

Before I could move, her bony hand dug into my tummy and I was yanked up in the air. She didn't speak to me. She didn't stroke me. She didn't ask permission to pick me up. 'He's a beauty. And big! Are you going to hold him, Imelda?' Her eyes softened as she looked at her daughter.

Imelda. The name chimed again in my heart as if it had been encrypted there. I stared at her. She gave a sob.

'For goodness' sake, what are you crying about now?'

Imelda turned to her mother. Tears streamed down her cheeks and hatred burned from her eyes. 'Don't hold him like that, Mum. He's frightened.'

'Don't be so silly.'

Imelda put her hands behind her back. 'I won't hold him like that. Put him down and let me make friends with him MY WAY.' She glared at her mother, who rolled her eyes contemptuously and put me down.

Imelda immediately lay on the floor, on her tummy. I meowed at her. I didn't know what else to do. She stopped crying. Her eyes shone with love, like those of my mum cat. She smiled at me while I sat, transfixed, watching her. She wasn't going to grab me and hold me up in the air. Imelda was going to bond with me. Suddenly we were in a private bubble, just the two of us.

'Come to me, baby cat,' she whispered. 'You're a darling and I want to be friends with you.'

She waited, hardly breathing, her eyes full of light, and it gave me time to figure out what to do. My tail went up by itself and I walked towards Imelda. I think she actually stopped breathing as I stretched towards her, turned my little head sideways and kissed the tip of her nose. 'You're magic,' she whispered, 'and I shall call you Merlin.'

I climbed into the crook of her neck and purred in her ear and she giggled. I'd done it! There was no going back. Small and alone, I was to go home with Imelda and her cold-eyed mother. I hoped Chloe wasn't cold-hearted as well. And Brad? Would he want me? I immediately understood that Imelda wasn't the problem. Her parents were.

Chapter 3

Granny's Cushion

Anxiety was a new experience, which began when I was taken from my mum cat. I'd been a confident kitten, the most adventurous in our family of five.

I wanted to go with Imelda. I already loved her for her gentle, sensitive way of handling me. But the shock of leaving my mum cat overwhelmed me. My strong little body felt suddenly hollow, and even the air around me seemed hostile. Being in a car was weird. The sensation of speed. The glimpses of trees and houses streaming past the windows. The intimidating thunder of lorries and buses, so close, hemming us in. And no mum cat to run to.

Paralysed by grief and terror, I cringed in the back of the caged travelling basket they had put me in. The more I longed for my mum cat, the more I cried, doing impossibly loud meows, wanting her to hear me and come running to my rescue. I had no concept of distance and the speed of a car, only a gathering shadow of loneliness. It felt wrong. I was a nice kitten. A ginger kitten. Why should I have to suffer like this? How long must I endure the extreme fear and isolation? Would it be for ever?

'For goodness' sake, Imelda, can't you make him shut up?' Chloe hunched over the steering wheel. 'I can't believe a tiny kitten can make such blood-curdling howls.'

'He can't help it, Mum. He's only a baby. And he's terrified. I'll take him out and hold him.' She began to undo the wire door of my cage.

'NO, Imelda. I said no.' The car swerved alarmingly.

'I don't see why not,' Imelda argued.

'Well, you wouldn't, would you?' Chloe's hands were pale and bony, her sparkling rings pinching her fingers white as she gripped the wheel. 'You know how I hate driving, so just do as you're told, Imelda – please.'

Imelda gave a loud sigh, and Brad turned around and frowned at her, and at me, with fierce eyes. 'It's for a good reason. If you let him out, he could panic and climb all over the car. It could cause your mother to crash the car.'

'But Dad, I want to hold him. I can't bear Merlin to be crying like that. And he's trembling.'

Brad lowered his voice to a menacing whisper. 'Either you do as you're told, my girl, or we turn the car around and take the kitten back to where he came from.'

There was an ugly silence. I filled it with heart-wrenching meows. I didn't like this angry family.

'All right, all right,' Imelda said at last, and muttered something under her breath.

'He'll survive,' Brad said, more kindly. 'Why don't you put a rug over the cage? It works with parrots. Makes them think it's night and they go to sleep.'

Imelda did find a rug and, when she slipped it over the cage, I felt better. I couldn't see the traffic or the landscape whizzing past. But I was too worked up to sleep. I had to keep crying, hoping my mum cat would come to find me with sweet, friendly trills, her special way of welcoming us. How I longed to see her benevolent tabby-and-white face. I simply couldn't bear to be away from her.

'I know you want your mum.' Imelda's face was pressed against the wire door of my basket. I found it helped to look into her eyes. 'I'll be your mum, Merlin,' she said kindly, and I remembered we had bonded and how good it felt to have eye contact with another soul. 'We'll soon be home, Merlin, then I'll let you out. We've got everything ready for you. A new

cat bed with white fur inside, and some toys for you.'
She chattered on in a reassuring tone, her soft brown
eyes meeting mine with an unwavering gaze. I listened
between meows. 'A ball to chase, a catnip mouse and
lots of food – kitty milk and sachets of special kitten
food. I've spent all my pocket money on it and I've
been saving up for ages and ages.' She went quiet for
a minute, her eyes sorrowful again. 'AND,' she added,
'we've still got my granny's special cat cushion.'

When Imelda told me about the cushion, I saw a
bright flare of light around her head and a misty image
of an old lady appeared next to Imelda. My heart leapt
when I saw that she had a cat in her arms. I stared and
stared, drawn to the old lady who had a smile like
Imelda's smile, with dimples in her cheeks.

But kittens need to sleep a lot and I was tired. Even
the urge to keep on meowing was less and less powerful. My eyes were closing though I struggled to keep
them open. 'He's going to sleep,' whispered Imelda,
and I melted into a dream.

I didn't see us arrive at my new home. I didn't feel
myself being carried inside. There was only a vague
sense of being in a quiet, secluded home. Being warm.
And close to the slow beat of a human heart.

When I woke up, it was getting dark and there were
sounds I was used to, like the hum of a fridge and

the pad of footsteps on carpet and the swish of curtains being drawn. It was early summer and a bird was singing outside. It sounded like the same blackbird who had greeted the dawn in the place where I'd been born. Was I there now? Was my mum cat there? I opened my eyes and tried to meow. My throat was sore from crying and I was absolutely starving.

'Hello. You're awake, baby cat.'

I got up and had a proper stretch, arching and flexing my back. My paws tingled and I wanted to move. I wanted to roll and play. Where were my brothers and sisters? And my mum cat?

'I'll be your mum now,' Imelda said again, as if she'd read my mind. She stroked me from head to tail with a gentle rhythm. I liked it. I gazed at her and meowed. She smiled, pleased, and there was a twinkle of wonder in her eyes. 'You are the most gorgeous, coolest kitten. Ginger with green eyes, just like I wanted.' I stretched out and kissed the tip of her nose. I sensed her delight at my friendliness and the long shadow of my loneliness began to slip away.

Hungry, I nuzzled around Imelda's neck and shoulders, searching through her silky brown hair for something to suck. I found a button on her blouse and tugged at it with my teeth. She giggled. 'I'd better feed you, Merlin. Are you hungry?'

She carried me into what was obviously a kitchen and put me down on the shiny floor. Bewildered at the new space, I stayed close, rubbing around her ankles as she poured kitty milk into an earthenware dish and put it on the floor. I could hardly wait! I lapped eagerly and it was lovely. Then she gave me a second dish with a delicious dollop of meaty stuff. 'Your little tummy is only the size of a walnut,' she said, 'so I'm giving you really small helpings.'

After my meal, I managed to sit by myself and wash. It was a discipline I'd been learning and I felt proud to be doing it as if mum cat were watching me.

Brad came into the kitchen. 'Oh, he did survive then?' He squatted down to inspect me.

'Don't hold him up in the air, Dad,' Imelda said. 'He's calming down but it's been a huge trauma for him.'

'I won't. Promise.' Brad stroked me with a big, rough finger. 'He's a beautiful kitten. Beautiful. Let's hope he doesn't wind your mother up too much.'

Imelda nodded.

'And don't you wind her up either.' Brad looked up at his daughter and I noticed his eyes were actually quite nice. He was more at ease when Chloe wasn't there. 'Your mother's lying down upstairs. The driving was hard for her.'

Imelda nodded again. Silent thoughts seemed to be passing between them.

'I hope you realise what an effort this is for your mother,' Brad said. 'She always vowed she'd never keep a cat. She doesn't dislike them, if they're friendly, but she's . . . well, you know what she's like.'

Imelda sighed. She rolled her eyes. 'Emotionally fragile.'

Brad stood up. 'That's about it.' He frowned and opened his mouth to say something else but Imelda held up her hand to stop him.

'Don't have a go at me, Dad.'

'OK, OK, let's get this kitten settled. How about me ordering a takeaway?'

'Mmm! Yes, please. Pizza for me.'

While Brad was gone, Imelda took me into the family living room. I followed her willingly but I didn't want more cuddles. I wanted to play as we'd always done in the early evening, the five of us – sometimes our mum cat would join in. But now I realised forlornly I would have to play on my own. Imelda had some toys for me but I wasn't interested.

I needed to explore this big room. It had lots of plants in pots. I walked around and inspected them, thinking they would be fun to play with. I could leap and make the leaves swing. I could even tear them off and drag them under the sofa.

The curtains looked interesting. I loved to climb, and the heavy, textured fabric would be perfect. I'd go as high as I dared and get them swinging. I surveyed the bookshelves and figured out the way to climb them. My claws would need to be sharp. I gazed around at the furniture. Oh, I was going to have fun in this magnificent room. But tonight I was too tired from the trauma of being uprooted.

'Not on the bed, please,' Chloe said later as she reluctantly agreed to let Imelda have me in her bedroom.

'OK, Mum.'

But the minute Chloe had gone downstairs, I tumbled out of my new fluffy cat bed and clambered up the duvet and into bed with Imelda. She was waiting for me and I sat on the pillow beside her and looked in astonishment at the book she was reading. I'd never seen a book before. It reminded me of a bird, because of the way its mysterious pages fluttered. 'This book is about King Arthur,' Imelda told me, pointing at the picture on the cover, 'and there he is, on his horse.'

She sounded excited, so I eyed the picture cautiously. I couldn't make sense of it and the 'horse' seemed to dance before my eyes. I patted its head to see if it was real, and it wasn't, but I listened anyway to what Imelda was telling me. She turned the page and showed me another picture. I stared and stared because it looked like a garden gnome we kittens had played with back home. 'You like him, do you?' Imelda said, pleased. 'Because he's a wizard, and he was King Arthur's friend, and he was called Merlin, like you.'

My fur started to tingle along my spine and over my tail but I didn't know why the information spooked me. It was the way she said it. With drama. Wide eyes and a whispering voice. Then she said, 'AND there's this place in Cornwall, by the sea, where you can go and see the cave Merlin lived in. And Dad's going to take us there on holiday – one day. If . . . if Mum's ever well enough to go. It's called Tintagel.' TIN-TA-GEL. The strange name shone out at me. It had three syllables. Three meows. Three snappy little meows. I did them, looking intently at Imelda. 'Mew-mew-squeak.'

'That's right, Merlin,' she laughed. 'Tin-ta-gel. It's like a piece of music.'

The name rang in my brain as if it was important, like a seed being planted in my soul.

She shut the book and put it under the pillow. I was tired – it would be good to sleep on top of this exciting book. I made a nest in the pillow and curled up, lonely again, but comforted by having Imelda close to me, her head on the same pillow, her hand over me as we slept, that first night of my new life.

* * *

There was so much to learn in those early days. I got into trouble on the very first morning. My need to play was a creative force within me and playing alone was different from the mock fighting and chasing I'd done with my brothers and sisters. We hadn't needed toys. We'd had each other.

The morning sun flooded in through a wide window and made the pot plants sparkle. I headed for a tall palm in the corner, leaping and hooking those spiky leaves down, watching them spring back and glint in the sunlight. It was exciting. I pretended they were birds and the long green fronds were wing feathers. At last, I managed to snap one of the stems, and the green fan of leaves stayed on the carpet. I hid behind a chair and pounced on it. I scrabbled the leaves up with my paws. I rolled on my back and wrestled with it. I felt happy and free. Until Chloe came in.

She gave a scream. 'You little MONSTER. What have you done to my plant?'

I froze on my back in the middle of a wrestle. Chloe leaned over me with a slow-burning fury in her cold eyes. She hissed at me and clapped her hands. It startled me for a moment, and then I continued playing.

'You BAD kitten.' She came after me and grabbed me with unkind hands. 'NO,' she thundered, 'you are not to break the plants.' She airlifted me into the kitchen where Imelda was eating breakfast. 'I knew this would happen,' Chloe ranted, and dumped me on the floor. 'Keep an eye on him, please, Imelda. He's wrecking the houseplants.'

'Mum, he's only little. He doesn't understand.'

'Well, make him understand.'

'Give him a chance, Mum. He's only just arrived.'

'I do know that. But I'm telling you now, he is not going to wreck the place.'

'You're overreacting.' Imelda scooped me up and held me tenderly, shielding me from her mother's scowling face. She carried me into the lounge. 'He's broken one stem from one plant. Surely a dear little kitten's happiness is more important than a few droopy plants.'

Imelda was really trying to protect and guide me, and she loved me unconditionally. I saw that she was going to be a kind, loyal friend to me, and I resolved

33

to do the same for her, even though I was only a tiny kitten.

While they were arguing, I wriggled free and jumped down. Full of energy, I scampered round the chairs and in and out of the table legs. There was a glass door to the garden with long curtains touching the floor. They swung and kinked as I explored. I lay on my back and slid along the thick hem, my little paws pedalling madly. I heard laughter, and remembered something my wise mum cat had taught me about humans. *'Make them laugh, dear, and they'll love you for ever. Lay your ears back, kink your tail and look wild – like the wild cats we once were.'*

Inspired, I did some impressive leaps and twizzled around in mid-air. Then I belted around the room, over the sofa, and vanished into the secluded folds of the curtains. More laughter. Chloe, laughing? I was on fire! I did it again with variations, diving under an armchair and emerging wild-eyed and flat on the other side. I charged at the patio doors intending to sail out into the garden, and banged my head on the glass. Ouch.

More laughter and a little scream from Imelda. Annoyed with myself, I retreated behind the curtains and sat for a moment, my heart going so fast that my pulse felt like a string of beads.

I wasn't hurt but Imelda came to find me, and I pounced on her feet from under the curtain and went flying across the room again and into the kitchen, where I skidded over the shiny floor. After a few more crazy circuits, I was suddenly tired and wanted to sleep, immediately.

With the exhaustion came another wave of loneliness. My mum cat wasn't there for me to run to. My brothers and sisters weren't there. How could I sleep, alone, so alone, like an island? Sadness engulfed me. My tail drooped and my tired legs wobbled.

'Put him on Granny's cushion,' Chloe said, her voice softer from the laughing, her cheeks smoother, her eyes kinder.

'You do it, Mum,' Imelda said. 'Merlin's got to get used to you.'

Chloe picked me up, with care, and held me close. I studied her eyes. The laughter had brought a soft sparkle into them and I felt suddenly sure that Chloe was hiding a kind heart beyond her usual cold stare. We looked at each other. 'Aw, you're really sweet,' she said, but I was too tired to try to bond with her. My eyes were already closing as she carried me to an old wicker chair by the window and put me on a plush velvet cushion. It was round, with a comfortable nest in the middle. I settled down, glimpsing some of the silk pictures around the outer rim. There was a tiny golden cat, and a blue bird with a long tail, and some red roses, and . . . My eyes closed and I slept deeply on the marvellous cushion. I would call it a cushion of dreams. Perfect for a lonesome kitten.

In my dream, I saw the old lady again, with hair as white as my mum cat's whiskers. She had smiling blue eyes and dimples in her cheeks. In her gnarled hand was a bright needle threaded with silk. She was stitching the cushion, the silks shimmering as she embroidered the tiny, golden cat, the blue birds and the roses. The sewing went on and on, like a lifetime, with leaves of emerald silk intertwining. I purred and purred, and longed to play with the shining silks, but the old lady's eyes told me I must not.

'You must listen to your angel,' the old lady said.

I listened, and, sure enough, I heard her voice, clear and echoing in my dreams.

'You are here to help Imelda,' she said. 'But you're only little and you have much to learn. I have come to warn you, Merlin. There is danger in the garden. You are not yet big enough to defend yourself. There is a feral cat out there – you must always be on your guard. Be watchful. You will know him by his eyes.'

Chapter 4

Bully Boy

'What's the matter with you, Merlin?' Imelda lay on the floor and fished me out from under an armchair. I meowed at her loudly, leaving my mouth open for a few seconds of maximum impact. How could I tell her I'd never been outside before? I'd never seen the sky or smelled the earth. The outside world had been only a picture, behind glass. Sitting on a windowsill, I'd watched things moving out there, mostly birds, people and cars. I'd seen the trees dancing, the sky pink, or blue, or dark, like small pieces of a jigsaw puzzle.

On my third day, Imelda carried me out through the patio doors and sat down on the lawn with me. She put me on the grass and my paws sank into it, alarmingly, as if I might sink deeper with every step until I disappeared. At first, I didn't dare to walk on it but sat, bewildered, peering at daisies, sniffing and tasting the sharp smell of the grass.

'No,' said Imelda, as I patted a bumblebee who came close, the power of his buzz vibrating, tickling my eardrums. 'Bees are very important.'

We watched the industrious insect clambering about on a yellow dandelion flower, his folded wings glinting like glass, his black face mysteriously expressionless. He was the first of many creatures I had to get used to. Somehow, I would have to figure out whether I could eat them, chase them, or communicate with them.

I was happy in the garden and interested in everything. Until I looked up – and saw the sky. The vastness of it, the way the blue went on for ever, up and out, with no ceiling, was overwhelming. I was a tiny kitten. And anything could come plunging down out of that endless sky.

I fled along the path. The patio doors were open but in my rush to get in I tripped over the mat and grazed my chin. I cowered under the chair. The dusty, stuffy darkness of it made me suddenly miserable and I was glad to let Imelda rescue me. 'What were you frightened of, darling?' she asked, carrying me back outside. 'It's lovely out here, with the sky so blue and the warm sunshine on your fur. There's nothing to be afraid of, Merlin. I'm not afraid.'

I leaned against her and listened, and understood from the reassuring tone of her voice. The sun did feel good on my fur. I dared to look up again. The sky was still there. Swallows were criss-crossing the expanse of blue. It was OK. Why had I been so silly? It came back to the same old problem. My mum cat wasn't there with me. I must learn about the world on my own now.

'You'll have to find ways of surviving', Imelda said, 'without me. Next week, I go back to school, so I'll only be here in the evenings and weekends.' She gave a deep sigh. 'And I hate it, Merlin. I hate it. I want to run away, like you just did.'

Imelda went quiet and I sensed conflict welling up inside her mind. *My turn to listen,* I thought, and sat on her shoulder, purring.

'I hate school,' she said again. 'I get bullied, every day. They won't leave me alone. I try to ignore it. I try to tell myself it doesn't matter what they think of me – but it does, Merlin. It does, and it makes me feel like rubbish.' She sniffed, and stared down at the grass. 'And when you feel like rubbish, there's no point in trying. Every day is a nightmare and nobody under-stands. Oh, what am I going to do?' Her cheeks grew hot until her body shook with sobs. She kept pushing strands of hair away from her face, tugging them back.

I was terribly concerned. What could I do? Surely I was too small to be of any use. But I tried. Purring and purring, and rubbing my head against her, patting her damp face with a gentle paw. She seemed to appreciate it. 'You're my BEST friend, Merlin. No one else cares about me. Well, Mum used to love me but now she's too busy and too stressed most of the time. But Dad has never even liked me. He thinks I'm a waste of space. He teases me about everything. He wants me to be all sporty and brave, and I'm not. I hate games at school and Dad gets angry 'cause I won't join in. Once he tried to make me learn judo and I hated it. That was the day he really, really gave up on me. He thinks I'm never gonna be any good – at anything. And I AM good at caring for animals. I love them and I want to be a vet – but Dad just laughs at me. I don't understand why, Merlin. Why does he want to hurt me all the time?'

She lay down on the grass and let the sobs lurch through her. I wanted to play, but this was serious. I mustn't leave her. I was only a little kitten, but I cared.

But then something happened that made her sit up and stop crying. Something that made my fur bush out and my heart race.

The angel had warned me, and there he was – a hefty black cat with bitten-down ears and a scruffy coat. I could smell him. He was on the garden wall, glaring down at me, his angular yellow-and-black eyes loveless and menacing. Once we'd made eye contact I couldn't look away.

'What is it, Merlin?' Imelda touched my bristling fur in astonishment. 'LOOK at your tail!' She followed my terrified gaze and saw the cat. He hissed at me, showing his fangs, and kept his mouth open, yowling in the back of his throat. His neck was thick and bullish and I could see the curl of his tongue.

I couldn't move. Instinct told me I mustn't run. He'd get me if I did. Instinct told me to stand my ground. This was MY garden. Being small didn't matter. I had power too. It was in my eyes and in my strong heart and the fire of my ginger fur. I sent him a draconian thought. *You wait till I'm a fully grown ginger cat. You'll have no chance.* I hissed and spat at him, and managed to growl as well.

I was a tiger.

He didn't go but stayed on top of the stone wall. He seemed to know that Imelda wouldn't hurt him. 'Poor thing,' she said to me. 'He's a feral tom cat. He hasn't got a home or anyone to love him so he stalks around the gardens on this road, stealing food and terrorising other cats. The neighbours call him Bully Boy. Mum chucks water over him if she sees him.'

Even as she spoke, Chloe charged out of the patio doors with a bucket. She flung an arc of water at the cat, but he was too quick, disappearing over the wall. We heard the heavy thump of him landing and the thunder of his paws as he fled across the next-door garden.

'I'll get you next time, you evil old moggy!' Chloe yelled. 'Watch out for him, Merlin, he's a killer.' She came close and admired my bushed-out ruff of fur. She laughed. 'You're a fiery little puss – but stay away from him. You're too young to fight. He'd make mincemeat of you.'

'Seriously, Mum, because Merlin is a male kitten, Bully Boy would attack him if he got the chance,' Imelda said, stroking my fur down. 'When I'm back at school next week, you will take care of Merlin, won't you?'

'Of course I will,' Chloe said huffily.

'Don't shut him out in the garden. He mustn't be shut out when he's so new and inexperienced.'

'I can't be watching him all day. I've got work to do.'

Imelda sighed. 'Yeah, I get that, but it might be best to keep him inside until I come home.'

'Well, I'm not sure I can cope with him rampaging all over the furniture.'

Imelda didn't hide her anxiety. 'What we need is a cat flap. Can't we get one? Dad could fit it in the kitchen door. I don't mind going without my pocket money for a few weeks if we can't afford one.'

'We can afford one. It's a shame to make a hole in a perfectly good door. Dad won't like it and neither do I.'

'I think we should have one. It would make Merlin happier,' insisted Imelda.

'Look, you wanted a kitten and you've got a kitten, Imelda. You can't have your own way all the time.'

'I don't. If I had my own way, Mum, I wouldn't go to school – EVER. And don't give me the lecture about taking exams and stuff. I'd actually like to do that but how can I when the bullies won't leave me alone?'

Chloe nodded her head slowly. She studied Imelda's face. 'Have you been crying? Your eyes are red.' She didn't wait for an answer. 'Crying to that kitten, I suppose.'

'Yes.' Imelda kissed the top of my head. 'He's a good listener. Non-judgemental and kind.'

Safe on Imelda's lap, I considered Chloe. Why was she so stressed? I didn't understand. Only two things were clear in my mind: I didn't want to be alone with her, and Imelda needed my help.

* * *

Imelda went back to school, begrudgingly, and I managed to explore the garden on my own. There were plenty of hiding places. Overgrown paths and steps were covered in windblown petals from the flowering shrubs. In one corner was a pond full of very green water, and one day I fell in.

It happened when I was alone with Chloe. She seemed angry with me when I was only playing. She had a table in the living room dedicated to her work, which was often covered with deliciously slippery papers. I'd been pouncing on them and discovering how one sheet of paper would slide to the edge of the table, with me on it, then fly off on to the floor. Once on the carpet, the papers would skid beautifully, and the faster I ran and leapt on to one, the further it would skid. It was brilliant fun. With more and more papers on the floor at crazy angles, my game got wilder. I flattened my ears, kinked my tail and sped around the room, skidding under chairs and tables and crashing into the sofa.

If cats could laugh, then I'd have been rolling about with my paws in the air. It was pure fun.

Chloe didn't share my enthusiasm when she came through the doorway, hollow-cheeked and frowning. Her eyes turned dark as they swept the room, and she shrieked. I skidded to a halt and looked up at her.

I ought to be polite, I knew. So I meowed, nicely, and put my tail up, thinking she would smile.

Instead, she gave an anguished howl and clawed the air with both hands. 'YOU,' she squawked. 'You brazen, destructive kitten. Get out. Out of my ssssight!' She leaned down and hissed at me like a cat.

I didn't know what she wanted, so I stayed there gazing up at her. If that didn't work, I planned to rub around her cold, thin ankles with my loving little body. But Chloe seemed to actually freeze with rage. She went stiff and pursed her mouth shut as if she feared what further vitriol might emerge from it.

She stooped and picked me up with one hand, joints cracking. She didn't hold me nicely but left my paws dangling in the air. Bewildered, I turned my sweet little face to hers, thinking my charm would melt her heart as usual. It didn't work. She swept into the kitchen, flung the door open, and dropped me – yes, dropped me! – on the doorstep.

Astonished, and slightly miffed, I turned to her – with my tail up – and she shut the door in my face.

I was a ginger kitten. A nice kitten. With a kind heart. Fancy treating me like that! Now seriously miffed, I shook my fur and trotted into the garden. I wanted a drink, then a healing sleep. My water bowl was empty so I headed down to the pond, feeling suddenly lonely and tired.

The weather was unseasonably hot and thundery, with flies buzzing and ants scurrying around. The pond water was covered in a thick scum of green slime. I hesitated, not liking the smell of it. I wanted water, not slime. But it looked solid enough to walk on and in the middle was a patch of clear water. I stretched out a paw and tested the glutinous green scum. Was it really solid? I was very thirsty so I tried to trot gently across it. And that's when I fell in.

Head first, I sank into the darkness below the slime. Foul-tasting water went in my mouth, up my nose and in my ears. I kicked and spluttered. My fur became heavy. It dragged and pulled me down as I instinctively lifted my head and swam towards the light, even though my eyes burned and stung. I didn't know how to swim, but my paws knew exactly what to do. It was like climbing, but climbing through liquid where even the greatest effort brought no progress.

I fought until my face was up out of the water, and then I was disorientated, not knowing which way to swim. I tried to meow for help but only pathetic squeaks and gasps would come. No matter how hard I kicked, the weight of my wet fur was too much for me.

Round and round I went, getting weaker and more desperate. I could hardly breathe and the deep cold of the pond water numbed my limbs. But I didn't give up. I wasn't going to die. Was I?

The light in the garden changed. Shadows crept over the water. But there was light – a flare of shimmering brightness at one end of the pond. Then I heard an unbelievable sound. A cat. Another cat was in the garden, sitting within that flare of light – a tabby cat with a white face and strong white whiskers. I heard her calling me, with a loud, encouraging trill-meow, like my mum cat. I swam towards her and suddenly I was aware of my own strong little heart pump-pumping, like the hot flickering of a candle. My life, my light, my flame keeping me afloat. Swimming for my life, towards the love in the cat's eyes. Gold, pure gold, like my mum cat's eyes. Her voice, her warmth, calling and calling me until I was almost there.

Grass at the edge of the pond brushed the top of my head. My pads touched the mud. I crawled towards the stillness and the strength of the tabby-and-white cat. She had saved me – or had she made me save myself?

I was out, covered in slime, my fur streaming, my heart still faithfully beating. The leaves above me rustled and a freezing cold wind gusted through the garden. I lay on the wet ground, trembling with shock and exhaustion, wanting to sleep. I forced my eyes to open. I was alone.

Who would know where I was? Imelda was at school and Brad at work. Chloe was still angry. The anger drifted down the garden like a dark fog. She had shut the door in my face. How would I get in? I badly needed to get warm and dry. Imelda would come searching for me. But did I even look like a ginger kitten? Or was I a heap of wet fur, stinking of pond water, and too weak to move?

How many hours would it be until Imelda came home from school? I didn't know. Being so cold and wet was driving me into sleep. Was I dying? I closed my eyes and drifted into a semi-conscious, dreamlike state.

I didn't know that someone else was slinking through the garden on four large paws, heading for the pond with a sense of purpose. Another cat. Huge and silent, a look in his eyes. A look of intention.

In my sleep, I heard his quiet footsteps. I felt his breath as he sniffed me. Then he lay down beside me and arranged himself around my cold, wet, trembling body. I heard his purr, and it was loud. His warmth was awesome, and just what I needed. He stayed there, wrapped around me, purring and purring until I was warm and soft. I went on sleeping, aware of him licking me, just as my mum cat had done, cleaning and brushing me dry with his rough tongue.

Hours later, warm and fluffy again, I opened my eyes – and there he was, still purring, caring for me.

And it was HIM. Bully Boy.

Chapter 5

The Brotherhood of Cat

The gift of sleep locked me into stillness while the sunlight mellowed into afternoon. Bully Boy continued to shelter me, giving me everything he had. His time, his warmth, his protection, his surprising compassion and knowledge of how to heal and comfort a half-drowned kitten. His love blessed me with the kind of sleep I'd had with my mum cat, the five of us in blissful security and peace.

Warm again, I could feel my fur getting lighter, fluffing out as it dried. Most of the slime was along my back and tail and Bully Boy went on licking, still purring while doing what must have been an unpleasant task. I was honoured that he had singled me out for his best attention. My questions were put on hold while he gave me unconditional love.

When Imelda came home from school, there were raised voices from the house, and minutes later she was in the garden calling me. 'Merlin, kitty, kitty, where are you?' She sounded anxious. We heard her quiet footsteps on the path, then brushing through the grass.

Bully Boy tensed but stayed with me, zealously licking the last traces of slime from my back. I was astonished at how much better I felt. Despite his reputation, the big black cat had saved my life. His eyes were soft and twinkly – he looked almost beautiful.

I could see Imelda watching us, thinking herself hidden in the bushes. Bully Boy seemed aware of her presence. He kept glancing up, checking. Imelda had told me how she'd tried to befriend him, even putting food out for him. He wasn't afraid of her but he wasn't friendly either.

I peeped at Imelda and did a silent meow – a new skill I'd been practising. I wanted her to know I was OK with Bully Boy. She must have been able to hear his loud continuous purring. A mysterious light glimmered under the trees and around the pond making the grass sparkle and the leaves shine as they rippled in the wind.

Awe and disbelief shone in Imelda's eyes. She was watching the magic unfold. Witnessing a bully being kind and compassionate, doing a simple, menial task with great love.

Time stood still.

Then everything changed in an instant and the spell was broken.

'Have you found him?' Brad crashed through the bushes, intrusive and loud, his clothes covered in cement dust.

Imelda swung round. 'Shh! Don't disturb them. This is amazing.'

Brad paused but it was too late. Bully Boy stopped purring. He froze and his eyes hardened, reverting to the black-and-yellow fathomless glare of a feral cat. A lethal blend of fear and anger.

'Don't intervene, Dad,' Imelda pleaded.

But when Brad saw Bully Boy with me lying beside him, he roared with hate. 'Get off our kitten, you 'orrible, smelly old bruiser. Go on. Get off.'

Bully Boy didn't just scarper. He arched his back and lashed his tail. He growled in his throat and hissed at Brad.

'Leave him alone, please,' Imelda pleaded.

'You've got to be joking, girl.' Brad gave another roar and shook his fist at Bully Boy. 'Get out of here, you old fleabag.' He bent down to pick up a stone and Bully Boy took off, racing up the garden wall and over it.

I did my loudest calling meow, crying after him. I wanted to say goodbye nicely. I wanted to touch noses with the big cat who had been so kind to me. But there was no response. Bully Boy had gone, back to his lonely life. I was terribly upset for him.

But Imelda was there now, picking me up tenderly. 'Are you all right, Merlin?'

I clung to her blouse, pleased to see her happy after her first day back at school. I leaned on her and purred. It was my turn to do the loving.

'Is he OK?' Brad asked, inspecting me with his no-nonsense eyes. He looked tired and annoyed, his hands ingrained with dust from his job as a builder.

'I don't know.' Imelda took me to the garden seat and sat me on her lap, checking me over in silence.

'He's all spiky. See his fur,' Brad said, sitting down next to us. 'And he pongs!'

'Long-furred cats go like that if they've got wet,' Imelda said. 'This fur dries all spiky. It needs brushing.' She turned me over and I lay on my back watching the swallows flying against the silver-white clouds. 'And you're right, he does smell.' Her gentle hands examined my tummy fur, which hadn't been licked by Bully Boy. 'This is pondweed. Could he have fallen in the pond?'

'I reckon he did,' Brad said. 'You can smell it on him. That fleabag cat might have chased him in there.'

'No, I think he fell in.' Imelda rubbed my tummy and I grabbed her hand with my soft paws and kicked. 'You little poppet,' she said. 'What have you been up to?' The love I could feel radiating from her as she spoke made me happy.

If only I could talk. I wanted Imelda, and Brad – and Chloe – to know what Bully Boy had done.

Imelda seemed to know. 'I wish you'd kept quiet, Dad,' she said, 'because Bully Boy was looking after this little kitten. He was purring and licking him, like a mother cat. And Merlin wasn't upset – he was loving it. Weren't you?'

'Surely not.' Brad had a sceptical frown on his face. 'That wouldn't happen. He's a known troublemaker and a bully, that cat is. Terrorises the neighbourhood. He should be caught and put to sleep.'

'But he can still be good when he wants to be. Cats do help each other if they're in trouble, regardless of their status. Especially if it's a kitten.'

'I don't believe it. That cat could have killed our cute little pussy cat.'

'Yeah, he could have – but he didn't. He was looking after Merlin. Warming him and healing him. It's the way animals care for each other. They really do. I mean, they're like us, aren't they? Just 'cause they can't talk doesn't mean they don't help each other. It's the Brotherhood of Cats.'

'And were you helped by a bully today?' Brad asked.

Imelda shook her head. 'No.'

'I thought not.'

'But that's different.'

'No, it isn't. Ask yourself, if you were in trouble – real trouble, badly hurt or drowning – would one of those bullies help you? Think about it.'

Imelda sighed. All the happiness I'd brought her was leaking away.

'OK, Dad . . . Anyway, Merlin needs a bath.'

A bath! When I'd spent hours getting dry?

With Imelda in charge, I actually enjoyed being pampered in warm, sweetly scented water, then dried in a cuddly towel on her lap. When it was over, I was given a meal of my favourite mashed chicken. It was good to feel glowing and clean again, and the bad smell of the pond water had gone. My fur was bright and soft. But I worried about the sadness I still felt from Imelda.

Chloe didn't apologise. I would have forgiven her, like cats do. 'I cannot be expected to cope with his manic, destructive behaviour,' she said defensively to Imelda. 'You should have seen the mess. I took a photo of it.' She waved her smartphone under Imelda's nose. 'I had to get on my hands and knees and pick it all up, then file it all – again. It wasn't funny.'

'But you shut him out in the garden, Mum – for hours, without checking on him. He had no lunch and not even a drink. No wonder he went to the pond.'

'If he does wrong, he must be punished.'

'He didn't deliberately "do wrong", as you call it.' Imelda rolled her eyes. 'He was having fun. Don't be so Victorian.'

'Oh go on, blame me. Mums get the blame for everything. You're a very difficult child, Imelda.'

'I'm not a child. I'm fifteen.'

They glared at one another.

'And I wish I was sixteen,' Imelda said, ''cause if I was, I'd leave school and get a life – and a job.'

'I doubt if anyone would employ you with that attitude.'

'Well, what about your attitude? Everything I do or say is wrong. Why bother? And why take it out on poor little Merlin?'

'Playing happy families again, are we?' Brad stood in the doorway. 'I'm sick of you two always at each other's throats. Sick of it.'

I wanted peace. I wanted to be back in the garden, lying close to Bully Boy. Perhaps it was me who should run away. Run away, and live wild with my new friend, Bully Boy. I was only young, not yet a full-grown cat, but the idea had already seeded itself in my mind. Escape, in search of peace. Yet, I couldn't leave Imelda.

*　*　*

Summer rolled on and there were roses on the bushes and the joy of a catnip plant which, Imelda said, had been planted just for me. I ate most of it, snorted some of it, and rolled around in its remains. It was heady stuff.

As I grew, my play became faster and wilder, mostly in the garden. Climbing the garden wall expanded my world and brought plenty of exciting opportunities. Next door's washing was there for me to leap on and swing. A lady called Sandie lived there alone; she looked like a rabbit when she smiled. She didn't mind me swinging on the pink and purple sheets she hung out. She sat by her garden door and laughed. 'You're a beautiful boy, you are,' she crooned, and spent time stroking me from nose to tail. Sandie was a good friend but she wouldn't feed me. 'Go on, you go home,' she said. 'I'll get into trouble with your lot if I feed you.' Then she added, 'But you're a good friend to Imelda, Merlin. She's been a lot calmer and happier since she got you.'

That pleased me. I was succeeding and my reliable love was making a difference to Imelda.

There were places in Sandie's garden where I liked to sleep sometimes, and there was a mouse-run along the base of her wall. It gave me hours of stalking, fun and practice in case I did become a wild cat. Right in the corner of her garden was a deep nest in the grass under the hedge where I could smell Bully Boy. He'd been there – sleeping. It was his nest. I didn't risk sleeping in it, but scent-marked it for him.

Weeks passed with no sign of Bully Boy, and I began to wonder where he was and if I would ever see him again.

Imelda was my faithful friend, and I loved the time we spent together. She played with me, and brushed my fur, and talked to me. It felt good to curl up on the pillow next to her at night. She told me all her secrets, her dreams and her worries, and I always listened attentively.

'I want to be a vet,' she told me one night, 'but it might be an impossible dream. Mum doesn't think I'm clever enough, and Dad says I never stick at anything.' She sighed and started twiddling the ends of her hair, wrapping strands of it round and around her finger. 'They don't understand how difficult it is for me in school. I can't get on and learn because of the bullies.

How I hate them, Merlin. I hate them – and I'm not a person who likes to hate people. It's awful. It's three girls. Some days, they turn the whole world against me. They even turn me against myself. And the teachers don't want to know. They just say I'm whinging, or "imagining things". I feel like . . . like no one in school likes me. Mum and Dad don't even like me.' Her voice went down to a whisper. 'What's wrong with me, Merlin? What's wrong?'

I purred and butted my head against her cheek. I knew she needed to cry, with those big sobs, but she just sat there hurting. I sensed the ache. It was like a sword which had been plunged deeply into her, and no one could pull it out so the pain never, ever healed. It wasn't fair. How could I make a difference? It seemed impossible.

That particular night, I felt powerless and alone.

Imelda was kind and gentle and she adored me. I ought to be able to help her. Cats are good at kindness. But humans are such complicated beings.

It bothered me. Hadn't I come here especially to help Imelda? While she slept, I sat on the bedroom windowsill and gazed out at the stars. Where had I come from? Who was I? And why couldn't I remember? Surely I wasn't all alone with the daunting task of helping this sad, kind girl who wanted to be a vet.

The window was open to the fragrant summer night. The wind ruffled my fur and a memory dawned on me – of another place, and another time. I had been a shining cat, looking up at an angel of light so tall that she towered over the landscape, points of light streaming from her wings. She had called me, and I had agreed to give up my life in the shining lands and be born on earth as a kitten to help a girl, Imelda.

The angel had taken me to a river. I recalled it, suddenly, in dark and vivid detail – the deeply coloured swirling waters sparkled like the stars on this summer night. The River of Forgetfulness. I'd forgotten, but now the memories dazzled me as they burst into my mind.

'My voice will be the one that comes to you on the wind,' the angel had said.

So I faced into the night wind and listened, there in Imelda's bedroom – on earth.

I did hear the voice. I sat perfectly still, my whiskers stiff and glinting in the starlight, my velvet paws neatly together, my emerald eyes dilated.

'Merlin,' she whispered. 'Imelda named you correctly. Merlin, the wizard, the good enchanter. He had a healing touch. He had only to put his hand on the head of a wicked or injured person and they were instantly and effortlessly healed. You have the same gift and it will gather its power as you grow into a mature cat. The touch of your paw will give her peace when she is anxious, hope when she is in despair, and love when she is sad.'

I looked down at my front paws and believed what the angel was telling me. Most of the time, my paws were a neat set of tough little pads carrying me around, but there were times when my paws were open and soft, like flowers. I really liked them, and kept them beautifully clean.

Would 'the touch' work with Chloe? I wondered. The angel picked up my thought and said, 'This is not the time for me to answer your question. Chloe has her own life journey. We will talk about her later when you are older, Merlin. It is enough at this time for you to remember these three gifts: peace, hope and love.'

Her voice began to fade. Then she came back strongly and added, 'And the greatest of these is love. You are here to love Imelda – remember that, Merlin. Love is so easy to give. The way you purr and make a fuss of her is perfect.'

The words echoed into the starry sky and I was alone, excited, listening to the usual sounds of night. Owls hooting. Sandie's radio. The swish of cars on a distant road.

I didn't see the angel but I knew when she had gone. Far away over the silhouette of treetops and roofs, a golden crescent moon hung in the sky, and above it was a curve of tightly packed, shimmering clouds arched across the dome of the sky. Like an angel's wing.

* * *

After the inspiring talk with the angel, it seemed like a terrible disaster the next day when something happened to my right front paw.

Imelda had gone to school and I was playing in the garden, hiding in the bushes then darting out, steeple-chasing over the lawn and round the side of the house, over the garage roof and into the cherry tree. It was quite a circuit but I was full of life and energy. Through the living-room window I could see Chloe at her table, pale and frowning as she worked. Next door, Sandie was singing and pegging out her washing – I was eyeing it for my afternoon playtime.

I charged through the bushes and pounced on a dry leaf, which was skittering along in the wind. It was a spectacular pounce, really high with stiff legs and a loopy tail. I landed hard and a searing pain shot through my right paw. It made me cry with shock. What had happened to me? Limping, I crawled into a shadowy place against the wall and lay there quivering, hardly daring to move my hurt paw. My healing paw! Had I ruined it for life?

Breathing fast and whimpering with pain, I sat up and lifted my injured paw. Blood was oozing out from between my pads. I'd never seen my blood before – it was scary. To be frightened of your own blood seemed ridiculous but I couldn't help it. I wanted to go to sleep and forget about it. I wanted Imelda. I wanted my mum cat. I wanted Bully Boy.

But nobody came. I crouched there, glad of the cool canopy of leaves. *Look after yourself, Merlin,* I thought. *You're nearly a full-grown cat now.* Tentatively, I tried to lick my hurt paw but even the touch of my tongue sent new darts of pain shooting up my leg. Further investigation was needed and, bracing myself, I turned my pad over and nibbled, horrified to find something very hard and sharp was embedded there. My efforts to pull it out with my teeth were excruciating and the pain made me feel ill. I couldn't get it out. I fell over sideways and lay down quietly trying to recover, not daring to touch the injury again. A butterfly came and perched on a stone right next to me. It had red-and-purple wings and wise little eyes. I studied it as I tried to sleep. It kept flying away, then returning to the same stone.

Was it trying to tell me something?

Eventually I made myself stand up, on three legs. I hobbled through the bushes and down the path to the house – slowly, and making little growls of pain in my throat. If only Imelda weren't at school. Chloe wouldn't help me – and that was a desolate feeling.

I made it to the doorstep and collapsed on the mat. To my surprise, Chloe came out, her hard shoes echoing through the hall. She stood peering down at me and my bleeding paw, which was now swelling up and throbbing.

'Oh, Merlin.' She squatted down and I held my paw out for her to see. 'Dear oh dear, what have you done? Can I pick you up?' (That was a first!) 'You poor kitten.'

Chloe picked me up gingerly in her arms, carried me into the lounge and put me in my favourite armchair. I was surprised to feel her hands shaking. 'What am I going to do?' she wailed.

I meowed. There was love in her eyes. Love, and panic. And the panic was completely overwhelming her.

What was going to happen to me?

Chapter 6

Chloe

'Calm down, Mum,' Imelda said as Chloe nervously reversed the car into a parking space. 'You've done the right thing. It's OK. I'll take him in and you wait in the car and listen to Classic FM.'

'I can't cope with this,' Chloe whispered. She was white-faced and shaking.

'You don't have to cope with it. I'm here. Merlin is my kitten and I'll cope with it.'

'Thank you, dear. Thank you.' Chloe reached for a bottle of water. 'I'll take some paracetamol and codeine.'

'Have you got a headache?' Imelda asked.

'No. The codeine helps me calm down.'

Imelda got out of the car, holding me in my cat cage. 'It's all right, little cat. You'll be fine. You've been to the vet before. He'll soon fix your painful paw, and

I'm here with you. I won't leave you for a minute, Merlin.'

I tried to do a nice meow, but I was in pain and the car journey had been harrowing. Chloe had made a fierce phone call to the school and insisted on taking her daughter out of class. We were both glad to see Imelda. I wondered why she didn't drive the car as Chloe was in such a panic. We lurched through the heavy traffic, stopping and starting, and Chloe cursed and swore at everything. Despite being upset about my paw, Imelda stayed calm. It helped me to have her there.

The waiting room was scary. Imelda draped a scarf strategically over the cat cage so that I couldn't see the big dog who was there. (I could smell him.) And there were other cats, and a rabbit, all in cages like me. I felt too terrible to take much interest in them so I crouched quietly in my cage and Imelda gazed in at me with steady, compassionate eyes.

The vet was a gentle elderly man who called himself Uncle Bob, and he had a kind assistant, Connie. His cheerful voice made me feel better. 'Hello, Merlin. Lovely to see you. Aw, you're a beautiful boy, aren't you?'

'I'd like to stay with him, please,' Imelda said, holding me firmly on the shiny table.

'Course you can. I remember you from last time, when we did his injections,' Uncle Bob said. 'Told me you wanted to be a vet.'

'I still do,' Imelda said. She held me with both hands as 'Uncle Bob' looked at my throbbing paw. The pain was too great for me to resist but it helped to have Imelda's fingers gently stroking me behind my ears and under my chin. It was soothing. 'I think it's a pyracantha prickle,' she said.

'Hmmm . . . they're very nasty . . .'

I gave a cry of pain in my throat as he examined my paw and he stopped immediately. 'I don't want to hurt you, old son. It's gone in very deep. We'd better sedate you while we get it out.'

There was a lot of stroking and quiet talking. Then an injection that I hardly noticed. It was done lovingly, with no fuss. My body grew soft and floppy and my mind dreamy. The last thing I heard was Imelda's voice saying, 'It's OK, Merlin. It'll soon be over. You'll be fine.'

Sleep was a blessed relief and an escape. I felt no pain. I dreamed of Bully Boy, purring. It sounded as if all the cats in the heavens were purring for me.

I did wake up briefly to find the pain almost gone from my paw, and a bandage being fixed around it, like a boot. Everyone was smiling. I sank gratefully back into a woozy sleep.

I finally woke up to find myself back home on Imelda's bed. She was sitting beside me, reading the King Arthur book and eating her tea from a tray.

'You're awake,' she said, pleased.

I got up and stretched. My paw had completely disappeared inside a bright blue bandage. I hoped it was still there. I sniffed at it, and picked at the bandage with my teeth, making it hurt again, but it was a small pain compared to the one I'd had.

Imelda understood my anxiety. 'Your paw will get quite better and be just like this one,' she tapped my left paw, 'but you must leave the bandage alone. If you don't, you will have to wear a collar that looks like a lampshade.'

There was a knock at the door and Brad came in with two dishes. He'd brought my tea upstairs – and I was starving. 'Poor wounded kitty,' he said. 'I've been hearing all about it from your mother.'

'Mum is in a bad way,' Imelda said. 'She was in meltdown. It was like I was the parent and she was the child. She really shouldn't be driving – and she needs help.'

Brad sat down on the bed in his dusty jeans. 'She won't go to the doctor.'

'Why not?'

'She thinks he'll declare her mentally ill, if she asks for help. She does need help, I must admit. I've tried talking to her but she just clams up, and we end up having a row.'

'I'd noticed.' Imelda put me on the floor and I hopped on three legs over to my tea. 'What's wrong with her, Dad? What is she worrying about?'

'Everything,' Brad said gloomily.

'Especially driving.'

'Well, I've got some good news,' Brad said, and his eyes gleamed. 'I get my licence back on Monday – first day of the school holidays, isn't it?'

'Yes, six whole weeks.' Imelda looked unusually happy. She had dimples and colour in her cheeks. 'Are we going on holiday?'

Brad's eyes twinkled and he clasped his rough hands together. 'We are! Third week in August – AND, guess where?'

'Seaford?'

'No.'

'Hastings?'

'NO. Somewhere we've always wanted to go.'

'No – it can't be – is it Tintagel?'

Brad frowned and shook his head, but his mouth broke into a grin. 'Just teasing!' he said, and banged his hands together. 'Yep! It's Tintagel.'

69

'Oh, Dad, that's brilliant. That is SO cool.' Imelda beamed and did a wiggly dance. 'I can't believe we're going – at last. Merlin will love it.' She gave me a cuddle.

'We can't take Merlin,' Brad said, seriously. 'Surely you know that, Imelda! You can't take a cat on holiday.'

Imelda opened her mouth and shut it again. She went silent and sat down on the bed. She picked up the King Arthur book and started to read.

Brad looked at her furiously. His eyes turned to me and my bandaged paw. 'We'll talk about it nearer the time – and don't you get any of your silly, stubborn ideas, girl.' Without another word, he left the room and ran downstairs.

Imelda took me on to her lap. 'I am not going to Tintagel without you, Merlin,' she said, 'or they can stuff their holiday. Just as soon as your paw is better . . . you and me will go on our own.' She opened her laptop and tapped the keys. I watched, fascinated. 'There you are. Look, Merlin,' she said, excited as the word Tintagel came up on the screen. 'See, there's the ruined castle, and the beach, AND, look at this – Merlin's Cave! And there he is.'

She pointed and I stared, moving my head from side to side, trying to recognise something in the jumble of colours, mostly blues and greens. I followed Imelda's finger and at last I saw a face. It was that garden gnome person again but he did look wise and important. I moved forward and touched noses with him, and Imelda giggled in delight.

Puzzled, I meowed to her, and gazed into her eyes. Couldn't she understand my frustration, and my embarrassment at having touched noses with a glass screen? There had been no response, no breath, no smell, no movement. To a cat, the act of touching noses is a sacred and honourable way of connecting with another living creature in a peaceful manner. I felt she was teasing me with something I didn't understand. It was an insult. Annoyed, I sat with my back to Imelda and her laptop.

She went on typing away, giving me a running commentary on what she was looking at. 'I've got the road map!' she said, excited. 'Tintagel is a long way from our home, but it's not too far – about a hundred miles. I've got a bike and a backpack – we could do it in a few days, Merlin. How would you like to sit in the basket of my bike and go flying along the roads, all the way to the sea? If Mum and Dad go without me, I'd like to see their faces when we arrive by bike.'

Imelda carried me downstairs. 'I'm taking you into the garage to show you my bike,' she explained.

I was still feeling fragile but I sniffed politely at the contraption propped against the wall, its wheels glinting in the subdued light of the garage. 'It's the only kind of exercise I enjoy,' she said. 'Mum and I used to go for rides when I was little but I wouldn't go with Dad. He used to go too fast for me and moan when I didn't keep up.'

She tried to put me in the basket, which was clipped to the front of the bike, but I didn't like the way it creaked and wobbled. I wailed and climbed back into her arms. 'It's OK. I won't make you go in it, especially with your hurty paw.' Imelda gave me a cuddle and looked into my eyes. 'I'll never make you do anything that frightens you,' she promised, and carried me back upstairs.

What she did next was interesting. She took a shiny blue-and-yellow thing out of a cupboard and put it on the bed. 'This is my bike helmet,' she said, and giggled when I peered into the air holes. When my paw was better, I'd play with it – drop things inside and have fun getting them out. My eyes must have gone big with excitement. 'I know what you're thinking,' Imelda said. She turned the helmet over. 'There isn't a mouse in there.'

The upturned helmet looked inviting. I stepped inside. What a place to sleep! I curled up in there on the soft padding. It was exactly the right size for a kitten. It held me tightly while I fell asleep, enjoying the sound of Imelda giggling at me and taking a photo on her mobile: Merlin, fast asleep, in a bicycle helmet.

Later, in the night, I lay awake while Imelda slept peacefully. I thought about the stuff she kept telling me. She wanted to be a vet. That was OK. But she wanted a holiday, whatever a holiday was – and she kept telling me about the sea and showing me blue-and-white splashy pictures. I didn't know and couldn't imagine what exactly the sea was.

I longed to meet Bully Boy again and ask him some of the questions burning in my mind. He was an old cat. He'd been on earth for years. Would he know what the sea was like?

There was one thing Imelda had shown me which had a startling effect on me. She showed me a furry toy with no legs and a big smile. A dolphin, she said, and showed me how it leapt high out of the sea, and smiled when it was in the air. Then she showed me a film of dolphins on the laptop and it stirred some deep emotion in me, some forgotten knowledge, about the friendliness of dolphins. She turned the sound up and let me hear their voices, and I understood their language straight away. It was profoundly moving, and exciting.

I had only one reason to go to the sea: dolphins. I wanted to talk with them!

Would there be dolphins at Tintagel?

I was only a ginger kitten. With an injured paw. But I had big dreams. One day, I would go all the way to the sea to see the dolphins.

With Bully Boy.

* * *

It happened on a day of dark weather – when it rained so hard that the windows streamed with drops and water from the roof cascaded over the guttering. There was a feeling of foreboding in our home, as if the frowning sky had come inside and breathed its gloom through our living space.

My paw was completely better and I wanted to go out, but the torrential rain had turned the house into a cage, every door and window barred with silver rods of rain. Imelda had won the cat flap argument so I did put my head through that, but the ground outside rippled with puddles and their reflections. It was no good trying to go out. I paused in the kitchen, wondering where to hide.

A row had started at breakfast time between Brad and Chloe. It was bad and loud, and that's why I wanted to hide. Playing on the stairs was not an option, and Imelda was pretending to be asleep with her head right under the duvet. She had something called toothache and it was making her miserable. For once, she told me to go away and play on my own.

I discovered what fun it was to chase the rugs in the hall, and I'd just got them really rumpled up and skidding crazily over the parquet floor when the postman came sploshing up the path. He shoved a bunch of wet catalogues and letters through the letterbox. More excitement! I added a few to my creative play with the rugs. With some vigorous chasing, I got one of the letters to slide under the furniture and had fun lying on my side hooking it out again with a long paw.

'For goodness' sake!' Chloe flung open the lounge door. 'That's all I need! See what THAT CAT has done now.'

I'd been enjoying myself. I didn't feel like being apologetic, like a dog. I was proud of my strength and agility. So when Chloe clapped her hands and hissed at me like a snake, I sat innocently on the stairs and washed.

Brad laughed heartily. 'You little monkey,' he said to me. If cats could laugh, I'd have laughed with him, but I cheekily nodded my head to make my eyes sparkle with fun.

But the laughter sent Chloe into a frenzy. 'It's not funny. I'm having a hellish morning thanks to you – and I should be working. You KNOW that, Brad. I need peace and quiet.'

'Shouldn't have got married, then, should you?' Brad quipped.

'You're dead right, I shouldn't have,' Chloe's thin lips spat the words out. She wrapped her arms around herself, her hands digging into her sleeves. 'And I wish I hadn't – so don't tease me. How can I work today with you under my feet and Imelda lying in bed with toothache? She's got an abscess, but do you care? Do you hell.'

'I do care, woman. Stop blaming me for everything. If a gnat farts in the garden, it's my fault.'

'And don't call me "woman".'

'Well, what are you? A nightmare bundle of nerves, if you ask me.'

An extra loud splat of rain hit the window and a gust of wind rumbled the front door. I peeped through the banisters at Chloe. She looked like a starling beaten down by the storm, wings broken, beak gasping for air.

'It is NOT my nerves.'

'Well, what is it, then?' Brad demanded, his eyes mocking.

'I get these terrible headaches. I've got one coming on now. It's stress. Why can't you try to understand?'

'I've spent the last fifteen years trying to understand you. What have you got to be stressed about? You've got a lovely home, and a job you can easily do at home. I'm out most days on the building job, aren't I? And I earn good money. Never enough, of course, for YOU and' – he jerked his thumb at the stairs – 'HER MAJESTY up there. I'm sick of the pair of you. Moan, moan, moan.'

I knew Brad meant Imelda. 'Her Majesty' was something he often called her when he was angry. He stood there fidgeting, moving his weight from one leg to the other and pushing his fingers through his scruffy mop of hair.

'I know you earn good money, Brad,' Chloe said, 'but it's not enough to pay the mortgage and maintain a decent standard of living. Of course Imelda has needs – she's a teenager. And I'm stressed, whether you like it or not. I used to be a good, successful accountant before I met you, but trying to do people's accounts from home is a nightmare. Unless you want us to live in poverty again, you'll have to accept that I'm not superwoman. It would help if you appreciated what I do.'

'So you expect flowers and chocolates every day, do you?' Brad smirked.

Chloe narrowed her eyes. 'There's no need to be sarcastic. A few kind words is all I actually want.'

She marched past him into the kitchen. 'I need my painkillers.' Then her phone rang with its musical jingle and she darted back to answer it. 'Good. Yes. We'll be there. Thank you.'

'Dentist?' Brad asked.

'Yes, eleven fifteen. And, please, you'll have to take her.'

Brad groaned. 'That's my morning gone.' He shouted up the stairs. ''Melda! Get yourself dressed and down here, right now. Dentist appointment.'

I moved out of the way and he went upstairs, two at a time. Halfway up, he stopped and pointed a finger at Chloe. 'And YOU,' he said in a loud, angry tone, 'get a life, woman – and start being a real wife and mother. I've had enough.'

I ran to Chloe and sat at her feet, looking up at her. I knew something bad was going to happen to her. It was already in the house – a vibration I could feel in my pads. She needed me and I wanted her to pick me up even though she hardly ever did.

She looked down into my emerald eyes as I gazed into her soul. I touched her with my paw. Tears ran down her face and she did pick me up. 'Oh, Merlin,' she sobbed. 'I get so cross with you, but you are such a darling.'

Ecstatic at being given a chance to love her, I purred my loudest and kissed her hard, wet cheeks. She'd never let me do this before. I wound my paws around her neck and leaned against her, feeling the knot of pain deep inside her head. 'Thank you, Merlin,' she whispered, holding me close. 'Thank you for loving me when I've been horrible to you.'

Together, we watched Brad and Imelda going off to the dentist, the car splashing through shining puddles.

'They might have said goodbye,' Chloe muttered. She put me down and sat at her work table, taking deep breaths and holding her head with both hands.

I went up to Imelda's bedroom and sat at the window for a while, playing with my catnip mouse. The rain clouds rolled away and the sun lit up the wet garden. At last, I could go outside.

I trotted down the stairs. A menacing stillness had crept into the house. My spine tingled. Something was wrong. Why was I so afraid?

I padded quietly into the lounge and found Chloe lying on the floor as if she'd fallen from her chair. Her eyes were closed, her skin deathly pale, and she wasn't moving at all.

Chapter 7

Too Young for This

I'm too young for this, I thought as I sat close to the unconscious Chloe. My mum cat would have known what to do. Bully Boy might have known. But I was a young cat, still full of the unbridled wildness of kittenhood.

Time alone with Chloe had always been a worry, for both of us. My life mission was to help Imelda. So why did I feel responsible for Chloe? Perhaps because we had finally bonded, after all this time. Chloe had picked me up when I had silently invited her to, and she'd welcomed my love. Why was she so stressed? Why was there such a tide of disappointment, pain and fear in her eyes? Where was her inborn gift of joy?

What would I do, right now, if Chloe were a cat? I let the question lead me. First, I would be there. I wouldn't leave her. Next, I'd try to wake her up.

I stretched forward to lick her face around the closed eyelids with great tenderness. I started to do it, then sprang back. There was a barrier like a force field stopping me.

The feeling that had been lurking in the house since early morning made itself known to me. Its vibration made my paws restless. My whiskers became incredibly sensitive and alive, like the antennae of a butterfly. Sitting perfectly still was the right way for me to gather the gems of information I needed.

I listened intently.

Death was in the house. It wasn't in Chloe . . . yet. It was prowling through the stones and the timbers, through the water pipes and the electrical circuits.

I sat beside Chloe, tall and regal, my front paws neatly together, my tail coiled around them.

How could I help Chloe? I glanced at the window. The garden shimmered with wet leaves. Over the wall I could see Sandie's washing going up.

I made a quick decision.

Leaving Chloe stretched out on the floor, I shot through the cat flap, sped over the soaking grass and up on to the wall. I saw Sandie. My calling meow echoed over the gardens.

Sandie looked up at once. 'Hello, Merlin. Coming over to see me, are you?'

I wailed and wailed until she came to the foot of the wall, a puzzled frown on her kindly face. 'What's the matter with you, dear?' She patted her shoulder. 'Come on. You come and tell old Sandie.'

I hesitated. *No,* I thought, *it mustn't turn into a cuddle. This is too important.* I couldn't meow much louder. I tried a higher-pitched call, more like a scream.

'You poor cat.' Sandie reached up to me. 'Are you hurt or something? You've got such big, dark eyes – is something wrong?'

I touched her hand with my paw and looked towards our house.

'I see the car's gone.' Sandie peeped over the wall. 'Are you shut out? They'll be back soon, Merlin, don't you worry.'

I continued doing high-pitched meows, patting her hand and looking towards our house. I was devastated when Sandie turned away and disappeared into her kitchen. I flicked my tail and my spine twitched with frustration. I watched to see if she would come out again but she didn't.

Powerless. I was powerless. Nobody listened to a ginger cat. All those echoing meows – wasted. I sat for a minute, chattering in annoyance at the impudent blue tits swinging from Sandie's peanut feeder. They were getting on with their lives, and I wasn't.

Chloe needed me. I must go back.

I streaked across the lawn and burst through the cat flap, my paws and belly fur soaking wet. Chloe was still lying on the carpet beside her work chair. She hadn't moved at all. I did a gentle trill-meow and settled down to sit with her. I believed she knew I was there, and the rhythm of my purring was, for her, a thread of light she could reach out and hold in the darkness.

'They'll be gone for hours,' Chloe had said when Brad and Imelda took off in the car. So I was surprised and a bit spooked when I heard a knock at the door, and then a key in the lock and the creak of the front door opening. A voice called out, 'Hello! Anyone home? I've got me key and I'm coming in to see if you're all right.'

It was Sandie! I was overjoyed but I didn't run to her. I wanted her to see that I was on guard, watching over Chloe.

'Oh no!' Sandie gave a gasp and came straight over. She knelt down and inspected Chloe, holding her limp hand. She smoothed her brow and went very pale and anxious. 'Come on. Come on, Chloe. It's Sandie from next door. Come on, wake up, darling. You've had a fall.' There was no response. Sandie looked at me sitting proudly on guard. 'You're a clever, clever cat, Merlin. You came and told me, didn't you?'

I did a long trill-meow.

Sandie jumped up and ran to the landline telephone. She pressed some buttons and asked for an ambulance. 'She looks terrible and I can't wake her up. Come quickly, it's an emergency. I know she's been getting bad headaches. Please, pray to God she's not dead.' To my surprise, cheerful little Sandie began to cry, and when she came back from the phone, her hands were shaking.

'Poor woman.' She took a rug from the sofa and tucked it over Chloe's still body, talking to her all the time. 'Poor Chloe. I knew you were heading for trouble. I knew it. I wish you'd talked to me. I'm here for you now. I won't leave you. You lie quiet, dear. Help is on the way.' She slipped a cushion under Chloe's head.

It wasn't necessary for me to be on guard now, with Sandie there, so I lay down and pressed myself close to Chloe's heart, purring and purring, doing my best to help. 'You're a wonderful cat,' Sandie said, 'and you're still only young. I wish I had a cat like you.'

It was oddly peaceful for a short while. Then I sensed change – an energy, speeding towards our home. I leapt on to the windowsill, nervous of this powerful, intrusive thing. A bright blue light came flashing along our road. An enormous ambulance pulled into our drive, its wheels crackling on the gravel. I could smell it! It wasn't just the disinfectant. This extraordinary vehicle had multiple smells, most of them human. The worst one was the smell of fear.

Sandie, on her way to open the door, noticed my bushed-out fur. 'Don't you be frightened, Merlin. These are good people – paramedics – they've got hearts of gold.'

I stayed on the windowsill and I couldn't help being alarmed by the two 'paramedics'. They were more alive than any of the humans I knew, including Brad, Imelda and Chloe. Fascinated, I watched in awe as they opened an enormous bag packed with shiny bits of medical kit. There were supple tubes that wiggled like snakes, packets which rustled and soft rolls of bandage. I could have had the best game ever unhooking the mysterious contents of that bag. *Don't try it, Merlin,* I thought. My tail twitched. It was hard to sit still.

The two paramedics, Connor and Todd, had cheerful voices. Calm and bright, soothing, like music. I hung back as they did some tests on Chloe, with curious wires and little lights and beeps. Todd did the tests and Connor squatted on the floor, manically tapping a pencil on a screen. *Like a woodpecker,* I thought, having watched one on Sandie's peanut feeder.

Their voices and the way they talked to Sandie reassured me. I trusted them but I didn't like the machinery. My namesake, Merlin the 'good enchanter', had simply touched a sick person and made them well. My right paw tingled – I'd tried it on Chloe and it hadn't worked.

But what happened next really, really upset me. They lifted Chloe on to a trolley, which creaked and gleamed. They tied straps over her, and a blanket, and wheeled her swiftly outside and into the pristine interior of the ambulance. They closed the doors tightly. The blue light flashed and the ambulance took Chloe away. Fast – with a deafening siren blaring.

I thought she was gone for ever.

* * *

Later that evening, the enormity of what had happened really hit home. Little did I know it was the beginning of the end for the family who had adopted me.

At first, it was OK. Sandie stayed with me and Imelda while Brad went on his own to the hospital. 'You drive carefully now, Brad,' Sandie warned as he headed out. But Brad didn't listen. Gravel hit the windows as he reversed the car out and he took off down the road with tyres squealing.

Imelda already looked shocked from going to the dentist. Her face was swollen and talking was painful. She was pleased to see me and I made an extra special fuss of her.

'He's a marvellous cat, Imelda,' Sandie said. She told Imelda how I had meowed on the wall to raise the alarm. 'It might just have saved her life. I do hope so.'

'So do I,' Imelda said. Then she went quiet and stared at the carpet, breathing in jerks the way she did when she was trying not to cry.

'We've got to keep hope alive, dear,' Sandie said, 'and if your mum's in hospital for a while you might have to grow up faster than you'd like – I mean, you'll have to look after your dad. Get his meals, do his washing and all that sort of stuff.'

Imelda shrugged. 'I hate housework.'

'Join the club,' Sandie said with passion. 'No one does my housework for me. I do me own. Have to. But you get used to it.'

Tension was building inside Imelda. Everything Sandie said seemed to send it up a notch. I kept on purring. But I was fed up with being a saintly cat. It was time for my mad half hour and I wanted it. Could I make Sandie and Imelda laugh? It was worth a try.

But before I could begin, Imelda's bottled-up feelings suddenly erupted.

She stared desperately at Sandie, her mouth pursed, her skin flushed.

Sandie looked alarmed. 'What is it, dear?'

For a moment, Imelda couldn't get the words out. She clutched the sides of her head with both hands. 'Mum isn't going to get better, is she? She's going to die . . . isn't she? Don't keep the truth from me. I'm not a child.'

Sandie wagged a finger. 'No, no, Imelda. You mustn't think like that. Where there's life, there's hope, that's what I say.'

'I don't need platitudes, Sandie. Tell me the truth.'

'I don't know the truth, dear. We can only wait.'

'But what could it be?' Imelda asked desperately. 'Mum was all right this morning – except . . .' She hesitated.

'Except what?'

'I'm not supposed to tell people, but she and Dad had a row this morning – about taking me to the dentist. Is it my fault, Sandie?'

'NO! Course it's not.'

'Dad's always telling her it's her hormones and she goes ballistic.'

Sandie tutted and rolled her eyes. 'Men!'

'It might be a heart attack or a stroke.' Imelda was getting more and more upset. 'She might die. Like Gran did. Gran had a stroke and she never even woke up. They took her into hospital and she was dead in three days. I miss her. Oh, what am I gonna do if Mum dies as well? I can't live on my own with Dad. I can't POSSIBLY!'

'Let's not think the worst,' Sandie said. 'We can only wait and pray.'

The tension was unbearable. I got up and stretched. I looked around for something to play with and noticed Chloe's work table spread with papers. I took off with a loopy tail, feeling explosive, needing to run fast. Round and round I sped, dodging chair legs and getting in a muddle with the curtains. Then I did a flying leap on to Chloe's table and skidded the entire length of it on a pile of papers.

But nobody laughed. Sandie's eyes twinkled with interest but Imelda got up at once and made a grab for me. She missed and I shot up the curtains and balance-walked along the pelmet, peeping cheekily at her. For once, she was cross with me. 'No, Merlin, you mustn't play with Mum's papers.' She started picking up the ones I'd used to slide across the table. 'These are bank statements. Mum will go ballistic.'

I did a rebellious meow and my tail twitched by itself.

'I know what you need, Merlin,' Sandie said, and she went towards the kitchen. She came back a moment later with a paper carrier bag. 'Can I give him this?'

'Go ahead,' Imelda said.

Sandie put the carrier bag on the floor on its side. It made intriguing crackling noises, the sort of sound that drives a cat bonkers. I reversed down the curtains and stalked the carrier bag, assessing the possibilities. I plunged inside it, fast, and it slid across the carpet with me in it. Then I turned around inside making an exciting range of crackles, and glared out at Sandie and Imelda with wild black eyes.

A chuckle from Sandie encouraged me – and Imelda's eyes were getting brighter. I emerged from the bag at full pelt, sending it flying with a kick from my back legs, and did a repeat performance, hearing the laughter building, and loving it. *Why not?* I thought. *Why not be happy when we're supposed to be miserable?*

I carried on doing it – with variations – and Imelda began to laugh despite her swollen face. I wouldn't stop until both of them were doing an ultimate belly laugh. That paper bag was the best fun I'd ever had and it was changing the atmosphere of the room where, only hours ago, Chloe had been lying on the floor.

It's amazing how a flying cat, especially a ginger one, can clear the bad energy from a room.

* * *

It was late when Brad finally arrived home. Imelda was asleep with me curled up on the pillow beside her. I'd had an exhausting day and I was glad of some peace. But even in my sleep, my ears flicked back and I heard Brad's car come down the road and turn in – slowly.

I heard him and Sandie talking in low voices, and then listened to Sandie going back to her home next door. Brad came upstairs, his footsteps heavy and slow. I could hear him breathing. He opened the bedroom door quietly and came in. I was too tired to sit up but I opened my eyes and gave a little trill of welcome.

'Thank you, Merlin,' he whispered, stroking my head. 'You saved Chloe's life.'

He leaned over Imelda and patted her shoulder. 'It's only me – Dad. I'm home now.'

She woke up at once and switched the lamp on to a dim glow. 'Dad! What's happened to Mum?'

Brad hesitated, then spoke in a low voice. 'She's . . . alive. She's being well looked after by the nurses and doctors and they say she is . . . comfortable – but still asleep.'

'But what's wrong with her? Dad, you will tell me, won't you?'

'We don't know yet and that's the truth. They gave her oxygen and set up an intravenous drip, and after a few hours, they said she was stable – so I came home. We'll talk about it in the morning, 'Melda. She'll be OK tonight, so go back to sleep and try not to worry.'

Imelda looked at him for a long time, her hand on his arm. 'Are you all right?'

'I've been better.'

Imelda hugged him. 'I love you, Dad.'

'Thanks,' Brad said gruffly. 'Goodnight, sweetheart.'

He left the room and went slowly downstairs. Halfway down, he stopped for a long time, then plodded on, and I heard him put the kettle on.

Normally, Brad would stay up to watch TV after Chloe had gone to bed. I was used to hearing the sound of his programmes and it didn't bother me. But tonight, I heard him talking, going on and on. His voice sounded like an endless lamentation from the heart.

'It's my fault. It's my fault,' he kept saying. 'Chloe told me she was ill and I was horrible. I've been a rubbish husband. I love my wife. I love her and I want her back. I'll never forgive myself. Never. Never ever. Please don't let her die. Please, God. I'll do anything, ANYTHING to bring her home.'

I debated whether to go downstairs to comfort him but I needed sleep to restore my own energy. I'd done a hard day's work.

Chapter 8

Business as Usual

'What's this? A burnt offering?' Brad said next morning when Imelda, her face still swollen, handed him a plate of incinerated bacon, blackened toast and a leathery fried egg.

'Sorry, Dad. I hate frying pans. I really hate them.' Imelda was hot and flustered. She'd got up early full of good intentions and nothing seemed to be working. 'It's the best I can do.'

Brad made a face and picked up a stiff piece of bacon. 'You could bag this up and sell it as pork scratchings.'

I sat on the doormat, washing. Brad's attempts to make jokes were falling flat. 'Don't have a go at me,' Imelda pleaded. 'We should try to be nice to each other.'

Brad sat with his knife and fork in the air, ignoring his plate of food, staring out into the garden. 'Yeah, OK,' he mumbled. Then he saw Imelda's hurt expression and the lamentation began again. 'I'm sorry, 'Melda. Sorry. Sorry. Sorry. I blame myself for everything. What happened to your mum – it might never have happened if I hadn't been so sarcastic and mean to her. I'm not proud of myself.' He pushed his plate away and sat with his head in his hands. 'It's all my fault. From way back, I've been hurting the woman I love. Deep down, I . . . I don't believe in myself, see? So I try to be smart – and this is where it's got me!'

Imelda looked at him caringly. 'Aw, Dad, don't beat yourself up. Mum would want us to stay strong and be kind to each other – wouldn't she?'

Brad nodded, tight-lipped, unable to answer. He pushed his plate away. 'I really don't want this. See if Merlin wants it.'

I didn't. I don't like charcoal.

'I'll go to the hospital first,' Brad said. 'You stay home. Sandie's there if you need someone. She said to tell you that.'

'I've got Merlin,' Imelda said. 'But can't I come with you to see Mum? Please?'

'Not today. Once she's awake and we've got a diagnosis, then you can come. Make her a card – she'll love that.'

Imelda pouted. 'Since when did she love anything?' she said bitterly.

'She's very moody.' Brad looked thoughtful. 'But she doesn't like me telling her that. She has changed so much in the last year or so. She used to be a lovely person – everyone loved her. Now her friends don't come near her. It's been hard for you too, I know.'

'Yep.' They exchanged a silent glance.

'I'll tell you one thing for sure,' Brad said, getting up. 'You can forget going to Tintagel. There's no way we can go.'

Imelda's eyes filled with disappointment. 'Yeah, I understand.'

'You don't sound like you understand.'

'It's just that I've wanted to go there for years, Dad. It's important to me.'

'Well, get over it. I'm off to see if your mother is still alive,' Brad shouted, and Imelda looked upset again.

Alarmed at the loud voices, I stopped washing and crept into the living room and under the sofa. I crouched in the dusty darkness feeling suddenly unwanted and alone. I made myself as small as possible and kept quiet, hoping I wouldn't be discovered. It was my home too and the one thing I hated was human anger. The shouting hurt my highly sensitive ears – a lot – it actually gave me a headache. Human anger was like a storm cloud which had come indoors.

My mouth was dry with fear and I wanted a drink. Would I have to spend the day under this fusty sofa? I quivered when there was more shouting and a crash that made the light fittings swing. The noise and the rage of it went right through my fur. My paws trembled and my heartbeat went crazy.

I wanted my mum cat. I wanted to be outside on the green, quiet earth. I was filled with sadness.

I heard Imelda stomping upstairs. I heard Brad slam the front door so hard that something else crashed to the floor. I heard him drive off, too fast, in the car.

And then there was silence.

I started to breathe again, quietly. I wanted my angel – but I didn't think an angel would come under the sofa.

*   *   *

There were times when Imelda would just lie on her bed and fall into a deep sleep in the middle of the day, and it usually happened when she was sad. I stayed hidden until it was quiet, then eased myself out and stretched. Sunlight streamed in through the lounge windows, making large yellow diamonds on the carpet.

I picked my way over the kitchen floor to the cat flap, through bits of broken china and the scattered remains of Brad's toast and bacon. A mist of anger lurked under the table and in the corners, invisible but malevolent. I needed to be outside where there was light and shining leaves and tiny, happy creatures getting on with their lives. I remembered the butterfly that had trustingly come close to me when I was hurt. It was time for me to learn more about the wildlife and try to hear the secret voices of those who would be my friends. Like the dolphins.

I was powerless to help Imelda, and that upset me. I sat down in the middle of the lawn, wondering what to do, when all of a sudden a strange feeling came upon me. I wanted to explore! Our garden was surrounded by other gardens, and so far I'd only been in Sandie's place. Next door on the other side lived a dog, so that wasn't a good idea – but over the end wall was a row of gardens, houses and a road. Beyond the road were tantalising glimpses of tall trees and rolling green pastures.

Navigation wasn't a problem. My psi sense was good, or so I thought. Instinctively, I could read the landscape and the sky. Deep in the earth were lines of magnetic energy and each one was different. The one below our own garden was easy. I knew it well – the line that would bring me home. My paws would remember its particular vibration. There were other clues, like the smells of a place, the direction of the wind, the flow of water. Follow a stream and it would take you to a river. Follow the river and you'd get to the sea.

I really wanted to do that.

'Merlin! MERLIN!'

I flicked my ears back. Imelda was calling me. She was upset and wanted me. She must be wondering why I was sitting in the middle of the lawn with my back to the house. I didn't turn round. But my dream was broken. I tried to claw it back, the precious knowledge I'd brought with me from the shining lands. My mum cat had given me her own version of it, blended with her wisdom and her experience of how the natural pathways of the earth were messed up by towns and roads and power cables.

'MERLIN!'

I didn't look round. My tail tried to go up, annoyingly, but I kept it down and ran to the far end of the garden, up the compost heap and on to the high, ivy-covered wall. The world beyond the garden shimmered with life. Undiscovered places called to me, to my spirit, on this summer day. I was filled with longing.

'MERLIN!'

All I had to do was jump down the other side and begin my exciting journey. But there was something in Imelda's voice. She needed me. I had agreed to be her cat.

I hesitated on top of the wall, listening to the sound of her running downstairs and out into the garden. I couldn't help it. I turned around and meowed. My tail went up by itself.

'Merlin, don't go over there. You'll get lost,' Imelda called.

ME? Get lost? Never.

She walked slowly, gently, down the garden towards me and I stayed on the wall. Her face was still swollen, her eyes stubborn and sad. But when she looked up at me on the wall, her eyes shone with love. 'You darling cat. I love you so much.'

That did it. I loved her too. I jumped down on to her shoulder and made a fuss of her. Imelda would never chase me. She'd never call me a 'bad cat'.

But would she ever understand my need for spiritual solace? I leaned on her, purring, as she carried me back into the house.

'You're my only friend, Merlin,' she said.

*   *   *

We both felt nervous when Brad's car turned up at midday. He came in sheepishly, the keys swinging from his finger. I stayed firmly on Imelda's lap in a corner of the sofa.

Brad's usual robust builder's look had gone. He was white-faced and seemed unable to talk. He sank into his favourite chair, unlaced his boots and stretched out with one hand covering his eyes. Imelda waited, tensely, for the news about her mother. I sensed the whispers and the questions in her touch upon my fur.

Without a word, Brad got up and padded into the kitchen where he stood surveying the shiny clean floor and the table laid for a meal. There were table mats, pretty plates and crystal glasses. Imelda had even filled a vase with flowers from the garden – roses, lavender and larkspur, the flowers Chloe liked.

A light dawned in Brad's face. 'Who did this?' he asked, incredulous. 'Who cleaned up and made the table so . . . so beautiful?'

'I did, Dad,' Imelda said.

'You did?' Brad's voice was hoarse and overloaded with emotion. He didn't smile but came back to the living room and crumpled into his chair. 'Thanks,' he growled, 'and I'm sorry, 'Melda, for shouting at you, and smashing stuff – and for frightening you, Merlin. I saw you run off when I yelled.'

I did my sweetest meow and blinked my emerald eyes for him, but Brad couldn't look at either of us. 'It really choked me,' he said, 'seeing the roses, and see-ing you'd laid the table for three.'

'I laid a place for Mum,' Imelda said. 'I thought you might bring her home.'

There was a silence. Then Brad took a deep breath. He shuddered and leaned forward in the chair, holding his head. 'She's not . . . she's not coming home.'

Imelda gasped.

Neither of them spoke for a minute. Brad looked into his daughter's terrified eyes and took her hand. 'Please, please try to stay calm. 'Cause I'm in bits.'

I heard the shock go through Imelda's heartbeat. She needed me and I was there, steadily purring. Business as usual, for me.

'I'll try. But tell me the truth, like, NOW, please. Is . . . is Mum dead? Is she?'

Brad shook his head. 'No.' He hesitated. 'But it's bad . . . it's bad news. Your mum had a stroke. She'll be in hospital for a long time – then in rehab. She might never be the same again. It . . . it's like we've already lost her.'

'Poor, poor Mum,' wept Imelda. 'I can't help crying, so don't yell at me. That's so awful. She must be scared. Dad, you must let me see her – you must. I'm not a little kid.'

'Yeah, of course I'll take you. She wants to see you. She can talk, thank goodness. We'll go tomorrow afternoon, if you like – and, look, about crying. It's OK. We're both going to cry a lot in the weeks to come. You're doing all right, 'Melda. I'm . . .' Brad glanced through the open door at the roses on the kitchen table. 'To be honest, sweetheart, I'm proud of you for what you did today after I was such a pig.'

'Thanks.' Imelda looked surprised. 'I feel better when you're honest, and when you're quiet. I've been through a lot of terrible stuff at school – with the bullying – stuff you don't even know about.'

Brad nodded. 'We've got to try to manage here, without Mum – and I must go back to work or there'll be no money coming in. Do you think you can cope with at least some of the housework?'

Imelda shrugged. 'I'll give it a go. It'll be OK until I go back to school in September. Mum will be better by then, won't she?'

'No. We'll be lucky if she's better by Christmas.'

A second shock pulsed through Imelda. I stayed with her, sensing the effort she was making to control the panic in her mind. She didn't try to speak but sat still, her hand smoothing my fur.

It wasn't over. Brad seemed to be struggling to say something else. His fingers drummed the chair arms and his feet shuffled. 'You might as well know,' he said, very quietly. 'It's not just the stroke. They did a scan, and my Chloe, my lovely Chloe, she's got a tumour. We don't know any more yet. They have to do tests – so we can only wait.'

Imelda stared at him. She got up and put me in the chair. 'I don't know how you can say that,' she said, her voice suddenly strong. 'How can you say "my lovely Chloe" when you've done nothing but criticise and tease her for the last two years? You're a hypocrite.'

Brad sank deeper into his chair. 'Go on, then. Hit a man when he's down.' He held his hand up. 'This conversation is over.'

Imelda went upstairs and Brad went to the fridge and got himself a can of something sour-smelling and fizzy.

*　*　*

That night, while Imelda was asleep, I sat by the window again, looking at the bright stars. I thought of my time in the garden and the enticing view from the top of the wall. The distant fields and woods. The silver streams and rivers. I vowed to explore them, one day, when I could break free of Imelda's constant need of me.

I felt like two cats. One was the goody-goody, devoted Merlin, always on hand to purr and comfort – the cat who had come from the stars on a mission to comfort Imelda. The other cat was earthly, and needed to play and hunt and roam the interesting world beyond the garden. It was the call of the wild in me, and it was strong.

One day I would go. Soon. I'd slip away quickly, before Imelda could call me back. Or I could go at night. The moon was full and bright, casting sharp shadows over the garden.

Suddenly a movement caught my eye. At the end of the garden where I'd been sitting. I burned with excitement.

On the wall, silhouetted against the starry sky, was an enormous cat, a black cat with bitten-down ears.

The words of the angel floated back to me. '*You will know him by his eyes.*' And I did. Bully Boy's eyes shone in the moonlight as he stared up at me. He remembered me. He knew where I lived. Was he waiting for me? Had he read my thoughts about exploring the world beyond the garden?

My skin began to prickle and my fur stiffened, puffing me up to twice my usual size. Should I go with him, right now? He had a reputation as a bad cat. But I knew a different side to his character. He was a big softie. Like me, he was two cats. Which one would he be tonight?

Chapter 9

The Call of the Wild

The decision to go was hard. Should I leave Imelda? She was asleep. Would she know I was gone? I checked her several times, even running back from halfway down the stairs. She stayed asleep, her hand on the pillow where I would normally be.

I kissed her goodbye, and fixed the memory of her in my heart. I sent her a telepathic message: 'This is something I need to do. I love you, Imelda. And I'll be back.'

On silent paws, I flowed down the stairs, through the kitchen and out of the cat flap. I trotted over moonlit grass, pausing once, my paw in the air, to get the vibes of the pathway, and to listen to unfamiliar sounds of night. It wasn't easy to move slowly when my heart raced with rebellious joy.

Bully Boy wasn't on the wall. Assuming he was on the other side, waiting for me, I dared to go straight over, dropping down through moon-splashed foliage into deep, scrunchy leaf mould. I sat down, tall and important, my tail twitching, my whiskers taut, as I assessed the strange garden and the house at the far end.

Where was Bully Boy? Disappointed, I tried a few tentative meows but he didn't appear. His scent was there and I had a prickly feeling he was nearby in the shadows, watching me with those feral, mistrustful eyes. Why had he enticed me out there?

I waited but he didn't come.

The call of the countryside beyond the gardens was compelling. I ran low to the ground, nervous in the unexplored garden, along the side of the house and into a wide street where cars were parked. I trotted on, across the road and down an alleyway. Bully Boy's scent was fading but the yellow glare of his eyes stayed in my mind.

At the end of the alleyway was a narrow lane bordered by a stone wall too high for a cat to climb. Massive trees growing on the other side towered over it and the pavement below was carpeted with fallen pine needles, pine cones and tiny domes of moss.

Preoccupied with finding a way over, I followed the base of the high wall. I was going to the wild wood and the wild wood was the other side of that wall.

There was a sudden scrabble of paws and an explosion of barking, which almost gave me a heart attack. A wiry dog was charging at me. With no place to hide and no time to think, I reacted instinctively. I pumped myself up, arched my back and hissed. I'd never been so terrified.

The dog's frenzied barking was torture. It hurt me inside my skull. Giddy with fear and desperate to escape, I had no choice but to face him. I wanted to go home. I wanted my mum cat. I wanted Imelda.

This hyperactive bundle of a dog wouldn't go away. If I turned my back and tried to escape, he would have me. He'd toss me in the air and leave me for dead. I growled and yowled, shocked at the appalling noises I was capable of making. They were high-pitched, loud and unwavering.

Understanding dawned. Despite the frizzy-haired dog's spectacular whirlwind charge, he hadn't touched me. He'd bumbled to a halt about two feet away from me. *He's all mouth and no trousers,* I thought, borrowing an expression of Brad's. On fire with confidence and fury, I hunched my spine, drew my lips back in a draconian grin and turned sideways to make myself look bigger. I inched towards him.

The dog's eyes were embedded in two whorls of kinky hair. Compared to the powerful stare of my luminous eyes and my stiff white whiskers, he was nothing. The instant I saw doubt in those eyes, I swiped at him. My paw whipped through the air and caught his nose with a sharp claw.

He cowered, whimpering. Merciless, I flew at him again and boxed his ears with both paws. I was astonished and elated when he fled like a hare, with his tail tucked under his belly.

Triumphant, I sat in the middle of the lane and washed myself, dead cool, as if nothing had happened. Perhaps I should have chased him. Next time, I thought. At that moment, I could have chased an army of terriers down the road.

I shook my fur and set off again. Further along the lane the wall ended in a pair of wrought-iron gates. I slipped under them. Immediately, the atmosphere was different and I was different. I was no longer the pampered pet with a predictable life. I was spiritually alive, attuned to the magic of this ancient woodland.

Silvery with gossamer, a footpath wound between banks of moss and tall trees, but I wasn't ready to explore it. I wanted to lie down on the sumptuous moss and absorb the ambience of the moonlit wood. I'd never seen trees like these – immense giants obscuring the night sky, the stars entangled in their branches. It made me feel small, but what these woodland titans gave me was a sense of peace, the deep peace of belonging. A feeling of welcome. Of coming home to the heart.

For a while, I just lay there and soaked it up, aware of the forest's secret power to heal and energise body and soul. Even the tiny baby spiders were spinning silk threads above me, weaving shimmering networks, millions of them working and swinging to the distant fringes of the wood.

It had been my intention to go home in the morning to Imelda before she had time to start worrying about me. The summer dawn came early and she was seldom awake until later when the sun was high. I hadn't intended to waste precious time sleeping but the cosy nights in bed with Imelda had become a habit. Despite my excitement at being in the woods, I fell asleep on the cushion of moss.

I awoke in the twilight before dawn. The wood rippled with music, the swish of leaves, birdsong and scurrying footsteps. I sat up and licked the threads of gossamer from my fur, uneasy. Something was going to happen.

The first shock came when a fox trotted past me carrying a plump white chicken in his mouth. He glanced at me and continued on his way, followed a moment later by the vixen, also with a dead chicken in her mouth. The rising sun lit her ruff of red fur and the pure white breast of the chicken. A trail of white feathers was left drifting around on the moss. The vixen didn't even look at me.

The next fright was an enormous bird which strutted right up to me on scaly feet. It had a round, russet-gold body, a long tail and a bright red-and-green head. It pecked around in the leaf mould. The minute I moved, it flew up, screeching, on incredibly noisy wings. Startled, I ran to the nearest tree, a massive beech. I sat on the lowest branch peering down at its gnarled roots, which coiled around the mossy base, little pockets packed with nutshells and dry leaves. One had a pool of water in it, a good place for me to drink, if I ever dared to get down. I was thinking about it when the vixen came trotting down the path. She headed for the pool and took a long drink. Then she gazed up at me, her chin dripping with water.

Remembering my success with the dog, I gave her a brazen stare. Her eyes reminded me of Chloe on that fateful morning – angry and desperate. She was thin and her fur was mangy. I felt an odd sense of empathy with her.

I tried a friendly meow. The vixen was not impressed. She started to do something weird. Crouching low, she ran around the wide trunk of the tree and each time she passed under the branch where I sat, she looked up at me hungrily. Round and round she went. Would she ever stop? Unnerved, I was growing disorientated from watching and trying to stare back.

I realised it was what she wanted – to make me giddy and cause me to lose my balance and fall from the tree. I couldn't look at her any more. The branch I was on dipped low over the ground, becoming narrow and twiggy. To survive, I needed to turn around and climb towards the solid heart of the tree.

Turning around on a narrow branch when you are dizzy and frightened is a tricky manoeuvre, even for a cat. That vixen knew exactly what she was doing. I dug my claws in and hung on grimly. I thought of Imelda and what she'd said: *'You're my only friend, Merlin.'*

I wasn't just a ginger cat. I was Merlin. I could do anything, I told myself. So I tried. One step at a time, I slowly turned around on the branch, wobbling and stopping, clinging and moving, while the vixen circled tirelessly under the tree, waiting for me to fall.

Facing the right way at last, I crept like a beetle into the heart of the mighty tree. There was a nest-like place in the fork of the branches filled with leaves. It felt warm and friendly and I settled into it, breathing fast.

I was very thirsty.

I hunkered down in the arms of the beech tree, my paws tucked under my body. I listened and realised the vixen had stopped running around the tree. Hopefully she would go away and leave me alone. Cautiously, I peeped out to see where she was and my heart sank when I saw her just below me, curled up asleep with the end of her bushy tail covering most of her face.

Somewhere in the archives of my inherited instinct was the knowledge that foxes were nocturnal animals, spending the daytime sleeping. Her eyes were closed but even in sleep her ears flicked. A meaningful sound would wake her up in a state of immediate readiness for action – fight or flight.

I had no chance of escaping from the tree. What if she stayed there all day? I'd end up having to lick dewdrops from the leaves and search the cracks and crevices for insects to eat. I was starving. If only I was back home, safely eating my breakfast in the kitchen.

I was in serious trouble.

My search for the magic of the wild wood had turned into a nightmare.

*   *   *

Far from home and trapped in the beech tree, I was sure I could hear Imelda calling me. Calling and calling. A ring of despair in her voice. Hurt in her voice. Hurt that I had caused.

Her voice sounded far away, muffled by the high wall and the woods and the distance between us. At times, it became lost in the roar of traffic and the voices of people out in the streets and gardens. It would be breakfast time at home and she would have discovered I was missing. I kept sending her thoughts. Cheerful 'back soon' kind of thoughts. I wished I had a mobile phone to send them on. I'd tap those keys with my paw and do some creative meowing. I hadn't meant to leave her alone.

What if I had to stay in the tree for weeks and weeks? I'd get thin and mangy like the vixen. What would Imelda do without me? I'd forget the way home. I might even lose my identity with no human around to call me Merlin.

How I'd longed to see the sunrise and experience the dawn in the wild wood. I'd been too stressed to notice it. But I saw the morning sun now. Perfect beams of light pierced the green leaf canopy like the spokes of a great wheel in the sky. Bees flew through the white beams like sparks from a bonfire.

Suddenly, my heart was thumping and I was on alert again. I stopped hearing Imelda's distant cries and listened to something closer, coming through the wood.

I sat up quickly, watching the dark spaces of the wood. Then I heard him – a bone-chilling yowl, repeating and repeating. The wood went quiet. The leaves froze. The bees stopped buzzing.

'You will know him by his eyes.'

Bully Boy's yellow-black eyes glared out of the shadows. His bitten-down ears made him look furiously angry. His fangs gleamed. His bushed-out fur made him twice his usual size.

I was excited, and honoured – and afraid.

Below me, the vixen sprang to life, yelping a barking scream of defiance. She lowered her head and crept towards the big black cat. I watched, terrified. Was this to be the mother of all battles? I was afraid for both of them.

Bully Boy didn't hesitate. He padded steadily towards the vixen. She had a bigger mouth with bigger fangs than him, a mouth that could carry a chicken for miles across country.

It was over in seconds and Bully Boy didn't touch her. He did it all with his eyes. The vixen cringed and backed away. Then she fled, her thin paws skimming the ground. He didn't bother to chase her but looked up at me with a softer, sunnier gaze.

Glad to be the friend and not the victim, I climbed down from the tree, doing purr-meows. My tail went up but his tail didn't. I wondered if it ever did. It was still lashing, slowing down gently, after the victory. An aura of confidence and sadness radiated from him. We touched noses, slowly, for a long moment of sweetness. My whiskers tingled and the air around our two faces felt highly charged with invisible sparks.

He was my first cat friend. He seemed old. Was I his first friend? I sent him the thought and his answer was, 'Yes.' Had he lived his entire life without a single friend? And lived alone like a wild cat? I felt compassion for him, and awe.

Sensing my thoughts, Bully Boy rolled over on his back and lay with his paws in the air. He trusted me! I remembered how caringly he had licked me dry when I'd fallen in the pond. Did he need some TLC from

116

me? I started to purr and once the purr was rolling, I licked around his battered old ears and the top of his head – places he couldn't reach himself – and I could tell he was enjoying it. He would love to be brushed, especially by Imelda.

Immediately, he picked up my image of Imelda and, at last, he began to talk to me. He understood language and we could talk, not like humans did but by telepathy, sharing thoughts in the silence.

'I let Imelda stroke me once,' he said, 'and it was lovely. It's the only time I've let a human touch me. The feel of her hand stayed on my fur for days. I can feel it now, if I try.' His eyes went misty.

'Imelda would look after you, if you let her,' I said, and my words were closely followed by a private thought, *But Chloe wouldn't – nor Brad.*

'No. Never. I couldn't live in a HOUSE,' Bully Boy said, as if a house were a disease.

'Why not?' I asked. 'It's cosy. I sleep in the softest place, on my own pillow, next to Imelda. It's softer than moss.'

The big cat regarded me thoughtfully. 'You are of a different race of cats who have evolved to meet the needs of humans. Except for Imelda, I hate humans, but I pity them too.'

'Imelda pities you. She calls you "that poor cat".'

117

'That poor cat! Me?' Bully Boy's whiskers twitched and his eyes danced as if he were laughing. 'But I'm a lucky cat. I can go where I like, when I want to. I live in the wood – I know those two foxes. I know all the gardens around here. And I go on journeys. I've been to the mountains. I've been to the sea. I've slept in caves, in hay barns and in hollow trees. I like being on earth.'

I stared at him in astonishment. There were questions I wanted to ask him so I chose the most compelling one. 'Did you come from the shining lands?'

Bully Boy froze. His eyes narrowed in a frown.

'I can't answer that question,' he said eventually, 'and don't ask me what my name is because I've never had one.'

'Don't you know who you really are?' I asked, incredulous. I didn't think it was wise to tell him that everyone called him Bully Boy.

'Names come from humans,' he said, 'and people have called me many names – bad names. It used to upset me but now I don't care. Those bad names used to make me angry but they also made me tough. People threw stones at me or buckets of water – that helped me fight for what I needed. I used to fight their cats, and their dogs – but now I don't need to. I can do it with my voice and my eyes. And . . .' The big cat

118

hesitated as if he had arrived at the door to a secret room in his heart and didn't know how to open it.

I waited attentively and rubbed my cheek against his. He gazed around at the beauty of the woods, the dappled sunlight on the pale grey bark of the beech tree and the tiniest red flowers on the mosses where we sat.

At last, he managed to put it into words.

'You are the first cat I have ever been kind to,' he said. 'You touched my heart that day when I saw you struggling out of the pond with your fur all wet. I didn't think I would know what to do, but I did. I *did* know how to be kind.' He looked into my eyes. 'Do you know where that knowledge came from, Merlin?'

'From the shining lands,' I said.

'The shining lands?' For a moment, Bully Boy looked like himself again as a glint of scepticism hardened his yellow-black eyes. The fur along his spine quivered and the tip of his tail flicked to and fro. High in the trees above, the crows flew up with raucous cries. The big cat's eyes softened again and a little sparkle came as he said, 'When I realised you were Imelda's kitten, I decided to be your friend. That's why I followed you, at a distance – to watch you explore the world on your own. I know what it's like. One mistake can ruin your whole life, so be very careful. Imelda doesn't want to lose you.'

'She said I was her only friend,' I confided.

'Then you must go home – and quickly.' Bully Boy stood up and stretched his powerful body. His black fur had a dull sheen in the woodland light. 'She is calling you and calling you. Can you find your way back?'

'I hope so.' I gave him a quick kiss on the nose. I didn't want to leave him.

He made it easy for me. He flattened his ears and did a giant leap on to the beech tree. Digging his claws into the bark, he climbed fast, zig-zagging from branch to branch. Then he stopped and looked down at me from the sky. 'Go on. You go home. I'm watching you.'

Mesmerised by the sight of him so high up among the leaves and branches, I couldn't move. Something held me there, a sense of light, a song, a voice whispering on the breeze. Bully Boy was a huge cat but he was tiny up there, cute like a black kitten. His eyes shone and his tail was up.

A blaze of light descended, down through the tree until it touched the ground, and I was drenched in its radiance. A thrill shot through me. I knew this light. It was the light from the shining lands, a tall pillar, sparkling as it brushed the ground in little curls and spirals. It was the skirt of an angel.

I nearly burst with joy. I felt incredibly small, like the gold silk cat on Granny's cushion. The wind whispered and I heard the angel's voice. 'I am holding him in my heart,' she said softly, and I knew she meant Bully Boy. He was being blessed, high in the tree.

I wondered if he knew.

Chapter 10

High Summer

It felt like afternoon by the time I reached the wall at the end of our garden. I was tired and very hungry. Coming home had not been easy. The roads seemed longer and more hazardous by day, populated with people, bicycles and cars. I saw the same dog again and this time I chased him down the lane. He was so frightened of me that he tried to jump over his garden gate and got his paw stuck. He yelped and shrieked, and a woman came running from the house. 'Oh my darling Popsie!' she cried, and quickly disentangled the frantic dog. She bundled him into her arms where he wriggled and whimpered, licking her face. *She loves him!* I thought, amazed, and found myself longing to be in Imelda's arms again.

I clambered on to our wall with the help of an apple tree and paused at the top. Imelda was sitting on the back doorstep staring at her mobile phone. She had one hand on her head, fingers pushed into her hair, which was unusually messy. An aura of deep despair clung around her shoulders.

I did my loudest, brightest meow, and she looked up, red-eyed from crying. Her mouth fell open and she jumped to her feet. 'MERLIN! Angel cat! You're BACK!'

I flew across the garden, my tail up like a plume of joy. My galloping paws made my meows all shaky. I couldn't get to her fast enough.

We were together again, and it was a blissful, unforgettable moment. I purred and purred and wrapped my soft paws around her neck. 'Where have you BEEN?' she kept saying. 'I thought you were lost, or hurt – or even stolen. But you found your way home, didn't you? You came back to me, Merlin. Thank you. Thank you, darling cat.' She went on and on saying the same things and crying while I snuggled close.

Brad appeared, a half-eaten burger in his hand. 'Thank heaven he's back. Phew. I hope we don't go through that again! Where've you been, Merlin?'

He leaned in close and I managed to give him a polite kiss on his big, sunburned nose.

When she'd calmed down, Imelda examined me carefully. She checked each of my paws and felt me all over. 'I'm checking you haven't been bitten,' she explained. She tweaked my fur. 'You've got burrs in your fur – and – oh no, Merlin! You've got FLEAS!'

'He's probably got worms as well,' Brad said, munching his burger. 'He'll have to go to the vet, 'Melda, and it's time we had him done, isn't it? He's probably been off making kittens.'

Fleas? Worms? Kittens? ME? I flicked my tail, annoyed with Brad for bringing my joyous homecoming down to earth. He broke off a piece of his burger and offered it to me. 'Want a bit? I'll bet he's starving.'

'I'll feed him. And I've got stuff for his fleas, and worming pills. He can't help it, Dad. If you were a cat, you'd get fleas too.'

Brad laughed loudly. 'If I were a cat, I'd be like that big black bruiser,' he said. 'I wouldn't be a carpet cat.'

I was carried inside and given a generous helping of my favourite 'Rabbit & Tuna'. Imelda gave me an egg yolk with some milk and a few of those hard little fishy biscuits.

Nobody mentioned Chloe. I looked at her empty chair and wondered what a hospital was like.

I was too tired even to wash after my meal. Imelda wanted to brush me and sort out the annoying fleas but, wisely, she let me curl up on the sofa for a long, long sleep.

124

She sat beside me, reading the King Arthur book. 'When you're awake, Merlin, I've got a really brilliant story to read you.'

Happy to be home, I drifted into sleep as Imelda gently stroked me. She was treating me so kindly. I snuggled closer to her, hoping she knew I was sorry that I'd left her alone for so long.

* * *

Summer rolled on. The sun was a deeper yellow and the gardens smelled of apples. Our life, without Chloe, settled into a routine. I was a happy cat, spending my days playing, eating and being close to Imelda. She seemed older and calmer now that she was 'managing the house'. Brad did try to be helpful. He went to work early every morning and got his own breakfast. Occasionally he came home for a quick lunch but usually he went straight to the hospital to spend time with Chloe. Imelda sometimes went with him but she always came home upset. She simply couldn't bear seeing her mother so ill.

'You're being selfish,' Brad said to her one day. 'Your mum wants to see you – it's important for her recovery.'

'What recovery?' Imelda said bitterly. 'She isn't getting any better, Dad, and when she does see me, she just cries – we both do – so what's the point?'

'The point is she's your mum,' Brad said impatiently, 'and if you go in there with a miserable face, it's going to make her sad, 'Melda.'

'I haven't got a miserable face.'

'Look in the mirror.'

'That's not fair. I feel things very deeply. You just don't understand and you never did.'

'It's not easy for me either, seeing my wife so ill. But what YOU don't understand, girl, is that we have to make an effort to smile and be cheerful, like the nurses do. They're angels, those girls. Seeing them every day has opened my eyes, I can tell you. To be honest, I'm ashamed to go in there with my miserable lump of a daughter. You need to grow up and get your act together. And' – Brad glowered at Imelda's indignant face – 'push your hair out of your eyes. You look like a Yorkshire terrier.'

Imelda was quivering. I could see she was hurt and so full of words she wanted to yell at her dad. But instead of coming out, the words went inwards, into her heart like poison darts.

I did something I'd tried before. With my tail waving high, I stepped between them and did a new kind of meow that I'd been working on. My tragic, plea-from-the-heart meow, strictly for occasional use.

Right on cue, they both looked down at me and I gazed from one to the other with my whiskers straight and my eyes sweet and reproachful.

It did create a moment of silence.

Imelda picked me up and held me nicely, despite her body being hot with fury. She narrowed her eyes at Brad. 'I hate you,' she said quietly. 'I wish I could run away and never come back.'

'Oh yeah, go on, then. You'll get taken into care if you do.'

'That's what you want, isn't it?'

'No, 'Melda, it's not,' Brad blustered. 'Of course it's not. For goodness' sake, girl.'

Imelda turned her back on him and carried me upstairs (where I didn't actually want to go). She slumped on to her bed. 'I meant it, Merlin. I'll run away – but not without you. I'll find a way.'

She opened her laptop and sat on a chair by the window tapping and clicking. 'I'm doing the research,' she told me, 'and next time he is horrible to me, we're GOING. I'm not leaving you with HIM.' Next, she opened a cupboard and pulled out a pink-and-grey bag, which she called a backpack. It had zips and toggles and lots of pockets. My eyes must have dilated with excitement. 'You want to play with it first, do you?' she said, and put it on the floor for me.

I went mad with it – probably too mad in a room the size of Imelda's bedroom. I knew that Imelda found my wild behaviour funny, and it made her happy, even when life was hard. First I attacked the pink-and-grey bag, lying on my side and kicking it with my back legs. I pushed it under the bed and had fun getting it out again, making Imelda giggle. Opening zip pockets was a skill I'd mastered so I did that too, and hooked the contents out with my paw. There was a bunch of keys, a packet of tablets, a notebook and all sorts of strange things. Right at the bottom was a tightly rolled pair of socks. I pretended it was a mouse and threw it down the stairs.

Brad was in the hall tapping his mobile phone. He shouted up the stairs. ''Melda!'

'What?'

'I'm going next door to see Sandie. Won't be long.'

'See Sandie? What for?' Imelda called, but Brad had already gone out. 'What's he up to, Merlin? He never goes to see Sandie.'

We sat on the bedroom floor amid the wreckage of the backpack. Imelda calmly reassembled it, replaced the things I had taken out and did the zips up. 'We'll pack this later when Dad's gone to the hospital. Then I'll hide it so that it's ready to grab if we need to run away. I'm going to put some money in it, and biscuits, and a Pot Noodle . . . and some cat food for you.'

I rolled on to my back and let her tickle my tummy, something she loved to do. 'I don't trust Dad,' she confided. 'One minute he's being mean to me and the next minute he's sorry and trying to make up for it. Why is he in there with Sandie? He's been ages.' She looked suddenly fierce. 'He'd better not be having an affair with her – surely not with Sandie? But I wouldn't put it past him.' She gave an exasperated sigh. 'Why, why, WHY have I got a dad like him? Why can't I have a decent dad like my grandad was?'

She got up and peeped out of the window. 'Oh, come see who's on the wall, Merlin.' She patted the windowsill and I jumped up there at once. We both stared down at the garden wall and my heart leapt. Bully Boy was there, resting peacefully on the sunny stones, his paws tucked under.

I meowed and he looked up at us in the window and blinked his yellow-black eyes.

'He's your friend, isn't he?' Imelda said. 'Shall we go down and say hello?'

I did a purr-meow. I wanted to go belting down the stairs and out to see Bully Boy on my own. But Imelda picked me up, and I let her carry me, thinking it would do Bully Boy good to see how I loved and trusted her.

Once we were in the garden, it was too frustrating for me to stay in her arms. I squirmed and she put me down. I dashed to the wall, hoping the big cat would stay there. He was pleased to see me. We touched noses and intense excitement pinged through me. Bully Boy was my buddy and my mentor.

Imelda noticed the rapport between us. She didn't march up to the wall. She crept, one step at a time, knowing intuitively how to approach a wild creature. Her eyes were filled with the love of doing what she did best – caring for animals.

I had a feeling something magical was going to happen, and it did.

Bully Boy was afraid of humans and I observed how his muscles tensed as Imelda inched close to us. I tried to reassure him with little purr-meows. Proud and majestic, I sat close. My presence would surely give him the confidence to stay.

Imelda stood still, close to us. She kept her hands in the pockets of the denim jacket she was wearing. *Look, no paws,* I thought. She glanced at me and a silent agreement passed between us. She knew I understood what she wanted to do.

Bully Boy's yellow-black eyes darkened with the anguished stare of a feral cat. His bitten-down ears flattened. One paw was in the air ready to strike. *Please, please don't scratch her.* His eyes were fixed on Imelda.

She spoke to him softly. 'Hello, Beautiful Boy. Are you OK? Do you need anything?'

No response.

'Have you got enough to eat,' she asked, 'and a safe place to sleep? Are you a lonely cat?'

She carried on talking to him in a sweet, musical tone and he listened, as if it WAS music.

Then she asked him, 'Have you got a pain anywhere?'

Her question must have awakened something in the big cat's soul. A glow passed through his hard eyes and he spontaneously made the tiniest of movements towards her.

'Would you like me to touch you?' Imelda took one hand out of her pocket and lifted it slowly and gently towards him. He was instantly on guard again. I felt sorry for him. How hard he worked to keep himself safe when it wasn't necessary. Imelda's soft little hand was so close to him. I prayed he wouldn't lose his nerve and scratch her.

The moment was fragile. I think I stopped breathing. But Imelda kept going, her hand moving a bit nearer and a bit nearer, until her finger touched him under his chin and began to stroke his fur.

Bully Boy gave a warning growl in his throat but it faded away as he allowed himself to enjoy the special under-the-chin stroke which most cats love. I don't know how long it went on but the three of us were spellbound, sharing the delicate time. Imelda stopped when she thought he'd had enough, gently withdrew her hand and said, 'Thank you, Beautiful Boy. Thanks for being my friend.'

I took a breath.

The big cat didn't seem to know what to do next. So I meowed and went to him. We rubbed cheeks and Imelda stood there smiling.

The magic came to an untimely end when Brad came round the side of the house. Bully Boy threw him a look of pure hatred and fled. I was sad to see his tail disappear over the end wall. He'd be heading back to the wild wood.

'What were you doing, stroking that old fleabag?' Brad demanded in a dictatorial tone.

Imelda lifted me off the wall and buried her face in my ginger fur.

''Melda!'

She looked up. 'I'm not a skittle, Dad.'

'What d'you mean you're not a skittle?'

'You're always knocking me over. Every time I'm happy or successful, you barge in and knock me over.'

'What's successful about stroking an old fleabag cat?'

Imelda didn't try to explain. Her face flushed, burning hot, and silent tears streamed down her cheeks. She started to walk away but Brad held his hand up. 'Wait, please.' He sounded guilty. 'I'm sorry – I've done it again.'

He put a hand on her shoulder and she twisted away angrily. Brad jumped in front of her. 'Wait. I've got some good news.' His eyes sparkled and he banged his hands together.

Imelda sighed. She paused, sceptical. 'What?'

'YOU' – Brad pointed at her gleefully – 'are going to Tintagel in October, for your half-term week – with Sandie.'

'Aw, Dad!'

'We just arranged it online,' Brad said eagerly. 'I felt bad when you were so disappointed at missing the holiday I booked before Chloe was ill. Today I got the cancellation insurance money back. It's too late to go now – everywhere's booked up until September and then you've got school. Chloe can't go, of course, and I can't – she needs my support. So I asked Sandie if she'd go with you. Is that OK?'

'OK? It's brilliant, Dad. Thanks!' Imelda gave me a little squeeze of delight.

Brad looked pleased. 'AND, by the way, you can take the cat.'

'WOW, WOW, Dad!' Imelda put me down and gave her dad a hug. 'We're going to Tintagel, Merlin! Ooh, I can't wait.'

Then she actually jumped up and down and Brad laughed and I tore round and round the lawn like a crazy cat.

Chapter 11

Tintagel

I sat in the window, like Cornish cats do, and gazed out at the sea. I couldn't comprehend the expanse of ocean. Imelda said it was water, deep, deep water where seals and sharks and dolphins lived. To me it looked solid, like a cobbled blue floor, a place where a cat could scamper and slide for a thousand miles. I liked the way it glittered with points of light. They danced and clustered into a dazzling pathway.

'Your neck's getting longer and longer, Merlin,' Imelda said, coming to the window. 'What can you see out there?'

The sparkles were enough for me. I could spend my life watching them. I hardly glanced at Imelda. She opened the window, just a crack for me to sniff the air. It was clean and salty. I held my nose to the crack and tried to sort out a cornucopia of smells which we didn't have at home. Wild, earthy smells of heather and gorse, a tang of fish – very fishy fish, nothing like the sachets of tuna Imelda gave me. There were animal scents – of cats and dogs, and wild rabbits. I tingled with excitement. I couldn't wait to go out and explore.

I tried to open the window wider with my paw and I looked round at Imelda and meowed. To my great disappointment, she shut the window and locked it with a key. 'Sorry, Merlin, but you won't be allowed out while we're here. I don't want to lose you.'

'Quite right,' said Sandie. 'Cats are not good at being in a strange place. But we're glad we brought you with us – you're a very important cat.'

I sent meaningful stares from one to the other and wailed. Surely Imelda of all people would understand my need to be outside. It was my world as well as theirs. Why shouldn't I go out?

'Anyway, it's October,' Sandie said. 'You won't like the cold wind from the sea, or the fog they get on the Cornish coast.'

'We might get a storm,' Imelda said, her eyes bright with anticipation. 'I've always wanted to see a real sea storm with big white waves and spray flying everywhere – and if we do get one, it will be good to be cosy inside making toast.'

They chattered on and I didn't listen any more. Had they made me endure the arduous car journey only to tell me I wasn't to be allowed out? But Imelda loved me too much to leave me behind. It was good to see her eyes shining as she talked. I loved her so much – but I hoped I wouldn't be shut in.

Apparently, we were in Tintagel in a 'holiday cottage'. It had thick stone walls, deep windowsills, and upstairs there were low, slanting ceilings. Outside was a square of lawn and, beyond the garden, a rocky hillside sloped down to the sea.

I didn't want the food Imelda put down for me. I flicked my tail, still upset about not being allowed out. While Sandie and Imelda were eating tea, I searched the cottage for an escape route. I even peered up the chimney and they laughed at me. 'Don't go up there, Merlin. You'll get covered in soot.'

There was no cat flap in the door. No windows open. I didn't want to purr. I didn't want to play. I didn't want my tea. I was a prisoner!

Miffed and sorry for myself, I sat in the window again and discovered something new. The birds in Tintagel were incredible. They were snowy white with grey wings and orange beaks. They spent most of their time in the sky and they could fly without flapping their wings, gliding and wheeling with breathtaking skill. I watched one take off from the garden fence. He sailed past the window and turned his head to stare at me with a glassy, yellow eye. I'd never seen a bird do that before. I was spooked when he kept doing it. Incensed, I stood up with my front paws against the glass. Hissing and growling, I threatened the big seagull each time he swooped to look at me.

Imelda and Sandie laughed at me, but for once I had no pleasure in their mirth. 'What's the matter with you, Merlin?' Imelda asked when I rebuffed her attempts to pick me up. I gave her my plea-from-the-heart meow and looked into her eyes. She could give me what I wanted. I ran to the door and did the meow again but she didn't open it. I felt betrayed.

After the hours of being cooped up in Sandie's car, I was bursting with energy. I needed a mad half hour. A VERY mad half hour. For once, my playtime was not joyful but angry. I needed to let off steam.

The rooms in our holiday cottage were small. I belted in wild spirals and improbable leaps; I attacked the stairs, which were steep and made of slippery dark wood; I ambushed the sofa from every possible angle; I slid across the kitchen floor on my belly.

Sandie had a cackly laugh and it rang from the walls. The whole cottage was laughing.

My angry play turned out to be funnier than usual and the laughter restored me, transforming my ugly mood into a good one. *Why be angry when you can be happy?* I thought, and finally I felt like myself again. A ginger cat. A nice ginger cat.

* * *

In the October dawn, I was awake hours before Imelda or Sandie. I headed downstairs, ate last night's supper and jumped on to the windowsill to wash and to survey the view of Tintagel.

I listened, amazed, to the music the seagulls were making. High in the sky, they circled in a whirling flock, soaring and weaving on elegant wings. Their cries sounded like a celebration, a ripple of music like panpipes over the town. They were constantly disbanding, moving on to a new place, then creating the circling music again, out over the sea, then inland over the village.

A sweet little grey-and-white cat appeared in the garden, gently stepping through the plants. She saw me in the window. We stared at each other for a long time and I ached with a desire to go out and meet her. She looked ethereal, and she looked at home. A Tintagel cat.

I fixed her beautiful face in my memory. We could have fallen in love and made kittens! But Imelda had taken me to Uncle Bob, the vet, and he'd done an operation on me to prevent me from getting a female cat pregnant. Neutering, he called it. Imelda said it would stop me getting into fights and ending up with bitten-down ears like Bully Boy.

After breakfast, I sat by the front door looking up at the handle and meowing.

'He's desperate to go out, isn't he?' Sandie said, concerned. 'Wouldn't he be all right in the garden?'

'No,' Imelda said. 'We absolutely mustn't let him out, Sandie. He's a young cat and he's inquisitive and adventurous. He'd want to explore. It's hard but I have to keep him safe.'

'OK,' Sandie said. 'You're in charge, he's your cat. I promise I won't let him out so don't worry, dear. You enjoy your holiday.'

'Thanks. You're a star, Sandie, bringing me down here.'

'Well, it's a free holiday for me, too. I haven't had a holiday for fifteen years – can't afford it.'

I continued meowing and gazing at the door.

'BUT,' Sandie wagged a finger at Imelda, 'we've got to be prepared for all eventualities, and you have to understand that if Merlin should go missing in Tintagel, we HAVE to go home at the end of the week – Saturday morning.'

'Yeah, I get that. Dad spelled it out to me. There's no more money for a B & B even if we could find somewhere.'

'If Merlin did go missing, we'd have to tell the local police and the RSPCA.'

'And Cat's Protection. And Facebook.'

'Someone would find him. He's such a lovely cat and so friendly. He'd go to anyone, wouldn't he?'

'Probably. But . . .' Imelda took a deep breath, suddenly engulfed by a cloud of sadness. I abandoned the door and ran to her. 'Aw, Merlin.' She buried her face in my fur and I made a fuss of her, purring and wrapping my paws around her neck. 'You're my only friend, Merlin.'

There was a brief silence. Sandie's motherly eyes were solemn. 'I hope you don't mean that, dear,' she said in a kind voice.

'I do.'

Sandie shook her head. 'No, no, Imelda, surely not. You're young. You've got your whole life in front of you. You've got more than I ever had.' She launched into a diatribe about her childhood and how poor she'd been.

Imelda had heard the story before. A look of impatience crossed her face, but she hid it well. 'I'm OK, Sandie, but it's nice of you to care.'

Sandie was still concerned. 'All right,' she said, 'but you promise me, girl, if you ever do feel you need a friend, you come to me. I'm only next door. You can come anytime. I mean that – anytime. It's gonna be tough for you when your mum comes home. I'll be there for you, and I won't tell a soul. Promise me?'

'Thanks.'

'Promise?'

'Promise,' Imelda sighed, stroking my fur from head to tail. Then her eyes shone. 'So what are we doing today? I want to see the castle, and Merlin's Cave.'

I looked at her. Merlin's Cave? Did that include me?

'You go on your own, Imelda,' Sandie said. 'I've seen it all before and I can't do those long walks now. I'll be happy pottering around, and I'll go to the shops and get us some pasties – and a tide table. You can only go in Merlin's Cave at low tide, so you be careful.'

I was disappointed yet again when Imelda set off without me, bouncy and happy with the pink-and-grey rucksack on her back and her hair tied in a thick pompom on top of her head. I sat in the window and watched her go.

'She'll be back soon, Merlin,' Sandie reassured me. 'It'll do her good to be out in the fresh sea air. She'll come back rosy-cheeked and happy.'

Sandie picked me up and stroked the back of my neck. She looked into my eyes as if she wanted to share a secret. 'You're not Imelda's only friend,' she said. 'I love her. I've seen her grow up and I know what she's had to put up with, and she's such a kind girl. I often wish she was my daughter. I'd be there for her anytime. And' – Sandie's eyes were suddenly fierce – 'I'd go down to that school and sort out those bullies.'

I purred, extra loud, and gave Sandie a kiss.

'Now you settle down and be a good cat while I go shopping,' she said, 'and Imelda will come back happy – you wait and see.'

Resigned, I settled down for a wash and a snooze in an armchair. Sandie went out, armed with a walking stick and a shopping bag, and I was left alone.

Homesick and disillusioned, I decided to amuse myself. I peered upstairs and saw the bathroom door wide open. My spirits lifted and I trotted up there and started a game with a plump roll of toilet paper, obviously put there for me. I patted it and watched, and patted, and watched, my excitement building as it unfurled and made loops on the floor. Digging my claws into the end of it, I reversed out of the bathroom and along the landing, and it came with me in a long streamer. Could I get it downstairs? I slithered down and it trailed after me like a ribbon – all of it! Very satisfying.

Sandie was not impressed when she came in with her shopping and found me winding the paper around the chair legs. 'You have had fun,' she said with a twinkle in her eye. I remembered how furious Chloe used to be with my antics, and felt grateful to Sandie for her good humour. Tutting all the time, she rolled my lovely paper streamer up again and put it back in the bathroom. *What a shame,* I thought, but I forgave her.

Imelda did come back, as predicted, absolutely glowing, her eyes shining. I'd never seen her like that before. It gave me a glimpse of the vibrant, caring young woman she could become. It reminded me how much I loved her. I'd done my best to be extra kind and attentive to her since Chloe had been taken ill. But now I could see that she also needed diversion from the devastation of her home life, something she could achieve best under her own steam.

'I've been miles down a rocky path to the cove,' she said, talking faster than usual. 'I paddled in the sea. The water is crystal clear and clean. It's brilliant. The waves are massive, like – you can't see the horizon because of the towering surf. I love it – really, really love it. I wish we could live here.'

'Don't we all,' Sandie said.

'And I found Merlin's Cave! It's actually a tunnel and you can walk through it to another beach. I picked up loads of shells' – she patted the pockets of her denim jacket – 'but it's the legend I find fascinating. It's in my King Arthur book. I know it by heart.'

Imelda was so magnetic in that moment. Sandie sat staring at her and so did I. 'Well, go on – tell me the legend,' Sandie said, and I meowed.

Imelda smiled in a way I'd never seen her smile before. It seemed to draw a golden circle of magic around the three of us. I sat bolt upright listening and, in the pause before Imelda began to speak, I could hear the sea. The massive waves were like a slow, slow heartbeat. They spoke to my soul.

'Well, Merlin was a wizard,' Imelda began, 'and he was sad because his people were always at war with one tribe or another. Nobody could live or work in peace. King Uther had just died, and Merlin knew the people needed a wise king to lead them. So he prayed and meditated – and stuff – outside his cave on a day like today when the sea was powerful. He gazed out at the water and beyond the surf he saw a burning ship – a ship in the shape of a dragon.' Imelda paused and two spots of rosy colour burned on her cheeks. I did a discreet purr-meow and the seagull glided past the window and peered in at us.

'Merlin thought the dragon ship was on fire,' Imelda continue, 'but it wasn't. It was a ship of light and it coloured the water pink and gold.'

Sandie's mouth fell open.

'Then Merlin stood on the beach and he counted nine massive white waves rolling in. AND when the ninth wave came, its waters gleamed with golden, fiery light. It surged up the beach and it brought a baby boy, right on to the sand, and he was perfect and strong. Merlin plucked the baby from the sea and he knew right away that the baby boy would grow up and become the greatest king in the land: King Arthur. Merlin waited until it was dark. Then he took the baby boy up into Tintagel Castle and gave him to Sir Anton, who was a friend of King Uther. He and his wife brought Arthur up and they pretended he was King Uther's son and heir, and they kept it secret – no one ever knew.'

Imelda sat back, glowing and satisfied with her telling and her attentive audience.

Sandie looked impressed, and very surprised. 'You should be on TV,' she said warmly. 'You sounded so professional.'

The atmosphere in the cottage and the change in Imelda inspired me. I hadn't quite understood the legend but certain images from it stayed in my memory. The dragon ship. The nine white waves. The baby boy.

It fired me up. I couldn't possibly go to sleep that night. While Imelda slept, her sun-kissed face peaceful, I sat on the bedroom windowsill watching the stars over the sea. The sound of the waves sent a powerful, rhythmic drumbeat through the heather-covered hills and the cottage walls. My longing to go out and experience it became unbearable. Some way, somehow, despite their efforts to shut me in, I intended to escape.

The days floated by and with each moment, Imelda grew brighter and happier, and I was glad to see her smiling. But I became increasingly frustrated. Monday, Tuesday. I was still shut in. Wednesday, Thursday. Our precious days in Tintagel were nearly over.

'It's our last day,' Imelda said gloomily on Friday morning. She glanced out at the sunshine. 'I want to do everything today, one last time.'

She didn't want to go home. Preoccupied with her plans for the last day, Imelda made a mistake, a mistake I'd been waiting for. I watched her go out. I watched Sandie go out. I crept upstairs – and there it was! An open window.

Chapter 12

An Open Window

The October sunshine warmed my ginger fur as I sat on the bedroom windowsill. Imelda had left it open, just a crack, wide enough for a paw. It had an iron latch with a row of holes and a peg and I'd watched carefully to learn how to get it open. Usually she locked it with a key, but today she'd forgotten to do it.

I tugged at the latch with my paw and, after a few tries, I managed to prise it off the peg. Immediately, a gust of wind blew the window open. Quivering, I peered down, calculating the jump I must make. It was an upstairs window, high above the garden. Had I ever done such a high jump? Never. Should I take the risk? Definitely.

Nervous, I moved from side to side, limbering my muscles, feeling the strength in my tail and my back legs. It wasn't a jump to be done recklessly. I didn't

148

want to land on the hard stone path close to the wall, or on one of the rocks sticking out of the grass. Thinking about it helped me, but it also made me afraid.

I prayed for help and listened, hoping to get some advice from my angel. I hadn't seen her for weeks. Where was she? I must do the jump before someone discovered me.

There was a sense of light shining around me, close, very close. The wind whispered and I heard the voice of my angel. 'I am with you, Merlin,' she breathed. 'You must jump outwards, not downwards. Kick hard with your back legs and I will be your wings.'

My legs trembled with energy. I reached down the cottage wall with my front paws. Then, with a powerful thrust of my back legs, I sailed out, my tail flying, my paws spreadeagled.

The moment of being airborne seemed to last for ever.

I landed (phew!) on an amazing cushion of grass, an experience not to be missed. I could have gone back and done it again.

Instinct made me instantly run for cover after my successful landing in strange territory. The seagull flew up from the garden wall, laughing loudly, laughing all over Tintagel at seeing a ginger cat trying to fly. I was not amused.

Recovering my balance and inner calm, I hid under the feathery canopy of a tamarisk tree. I looked back at the cottage and the open window, thinking of my bed in there on a pillow next to Imelda. If she was anxious in the night, or sad because she'd been bullied at school, I was always there, purring and reaching out a soft paw to reassure her.

But I was filled with crazy joy. Freedom! My freedom. I might even see Imelda when I explored. I left the back garden immediately and surveyed the expanse of wild hillside covered in pink heather, patches of turf and rocks. There were even a few butterflies, tiny blue ones and red admirals feeding on a clump of purple daisies. Close to me were the small, intimate details – ant hills and red-tailed bumblebees, stems of wildflowers with complex seed heads. The rocks fascinated me – their interesting shapes, so easy to climb, and stuffed with compact little plants growing out of every crack. There was an ancient friendliness about them. In the sun, they were warm, like heaters, and they offered many places where a cat could shelter. It would be possible to live among those rocks and feel safe.

I wandered, happy on the hillside, following the rabbit paths, tasting the peaty water from trickling streams and rain pools. Soon I had gone a long way.

I could no longer see the cottage and I'd forgotten to scent-mark.

Down and down I went, drawn to the shoreline. The sea didn't sparkle in the morning when the sun shone over the land but the water was a translucent green. Lower down, I paused, stunned by the power of the waves. The crack and surge of the surf, the boom as it slammed against rocks, sent a tremor through the hillside, and through me.

Awed, I settled on a sunny rock to watch. Why was it happening? How did the blue-green waters turn into dazzling foam which flew into the air like blossom? To me, it was a mystery I would never understand.

It could be fun to leap in the air and catch one of those flying drops of spray. I ventured closer. I reached the edge of the cliff where the tussocks of turf hung, broken, and the ground felt unstable. Sensing danger, I scrabbled to climb back, shreds of earth and grass entangled in my claws. Spray from a huge wave splattered my fur. It taught me a lesson. Those enticing white drops were not ping-pong balls. They were icy-cold water. I retreated to a safe, warm rock and licked the salty water from my coat.

I thought of Imelda. She didn't want to lose me. I didn't want to lose her either. She was my human who cared for me and needed my love. The cold sea spray, hitting me so hard, had made me remember the comfort of home.

Home. Where exactly was it? North-east, my psi sense told me, slightly to the left of the rising sun. Home was where Bully Boy lived in his hollow tree in the wild wood. But how far away was it from Tintagel? Again my psi sense told me – home was a long, long way. Endless days and nights for a cat. But it was OK, I remembered, we were going home in Sandie's car. Tomorrow.

All I had to do was get back to the cottage. If I could find it. Was I lost? The thought hit me hard. I'd been proud of my navigation skills. But today, in the euphoria of escaping, I hadn't done the work. I hadn't kept still and sensed the energy of the cottage. I hadn't scent-marked my route. I sat still on a flat, sunny rock and tried to see the cottage, and couldn't. *Stop worrying and enjoy the day,* I told myself, and turned towards the sea. I wanted to go close to it and touch the sand, sniff the shellfish on the rocks and look in some of the pools. I wanted to find Merlin's Cave and go in there and dream in the place of legend Imelda had described.

But up on the grassy hillside, a strange sensation came over me, an instinct mixed up with a dream. My whiskers were tingling. My fur felt ethereal, like an aura of gold ruffled around me.

I listened, alive and alert. Was it music? Was it Merlin, the enchanter? Was it dolphins?

It turned out to be the very last thing I was expecting.

Soft little footsteps, running to me. Stopping. Then a high-pitched purr-meow. I swung around, astonished, and saw the sweet little grey-and-white cat who had looked up at me from the garden. Her scent was perfect. She was tiny, but mature, graceful and full of light.

I think I stopped breathing.

I adored her from the minute we touched. She didn't hesitate but gave me the most exquisite kiss. Our whiskers brushed. Our fur turned to silk. Our eyes shone, green into gold.

'Where did you come from?' I asked. The little grey-and-white cat just stared at me.

'I'm Merlin,' I said and did my best purr-meow. 'Have you got a name?'

'Josephine.'

Josephine! Merlin and Josephine. It sounded good.

She quivered and her golden eyes danced with fun.

Divine joy sparkled between us and there was only one way to express it. A wild, crazy cat dance. Josephine started it with three high leaps sideways. Then she took off with a loopy tail, flying over the grass like a dandelion seed. I belted after her, dodging ant hills and rocks, the salt-sea wind fluffing my tail. She hid behind a rock and pounced out at me, springing high into the air. I saw her white belly and her little pink pads spread out like flowers against the sky.

We played like this for a long time, chasing and pouncing, both of us fired up and ecstatically happy. I was careful to be gentle when we pretended to fight but Josephine was fierce. She was little and she was going to win – so I let her.

When we were tired, she led me to a rock that resembled an armchair. A high back, warm from the sun, chunky arms and a seat made of bouncy sea pink clumps and grasses. We settled down side by side and did some purring. I was thrilled that Josephine wanted to be with me and her closeness gave me deep contentment.

Our first two hours together were filled with wordless love. We would need to talk but, like me, Josephine seemed to know that lifelong friendships were first created in the silence of the soul. So we closed our eyes and dozed together while the afternoon sun sparkled on the blue sea.

I believe the dolphins came close that day to share our happiness.

We both heard their music at the same time. We sat up, listening, watching the shimmering water beyond the surf. A gasp of joy went through me when I first saw a dolphin leap high out of the water, his indigo skin gleaming. Then the splash of crystal drops shining in the air. Then another, and another, in deep water close to the shore. Spellbound, I glimpsed the smile on the sleek creature's face. The smile and the bright eye. The message was strong and simple. A smile and a bright eye brings light to the mind and peace to the world.

What else did their high-pitched voices say to us? I didn't know and Josephine didn't either. Perhaps it would take years of listening and trying to understand their language. Imelda would want to do that with me.

Suddenly filled with sadness, I looked deeply into Josephine's golden eyes. 'I have to go home,' I said quietly.

'Me too,' she said. 'My house is not far.'

'I live far away,' I said, 'close to the wild wood, a long way from the sea. I wish I could stay with you, Josephine.' The poignant feeling made me ache inside.

Josephine sounded thoughtful. 'You'll come back here one day,' she said, 'and we'll play together again. I'll still be here.'

I was too sad to reply. Josephine noticed and rubbed her head against me, purring. She went on talking with her head pressed close to my neck. 'I'm committed to my human,' she explained. 'He's an old man called Theo and he's lonely. He lives alone and I'm his only friend. His family won't even speak to him. I'm the only link between them. I'm supposed to live with his daughter, Sarah. She likes cats and her children like to play with me. I don't know why she's so mean to Theo. I wish I could visit him more.' Josephine looked sad. It was as if the weight of the world had suddenly descended on both of us. 'If only I could talk to humans like I talk to you,' she added.

It was my turn to empathise. I lay down very carefully, pulling her down with my paw. I wanted her to lie with her sweet little head on my heart and feel my strong heartbeat, and she did. I told her about Imelda and how powerless I often seemed to be. 'But we can help our humans,' I said, 'if we do lots of purring, and stretch our paws over their hearts. Imelda is worried for her mum, and her dad doesn't understand her feelings. She's always happier when I'm there.'

Josephine closed her eyes. She wasn't asleep but was listening to my words and my heartbeat. I told her about Bully Boy and how he'd rescued me from the pond, and loved me despite his reputation. 'He was my first cat friend,' I said, 'and you're my friend now, Josephine.'

She lay still, taking it all in.

The sea wasn't sparkling any more. Oddly, it seemed to be disappearing into a thick, heavy mist. Josephine sat up. 'The mist is coming in, Merlin. We must go home – both of us. Now.'

I hadn't yet told her everything. The mist wasn't important to me. But Josephine stood up and stretched. She flicked her tail. 'The mist is very dangerous,' she insisted. 'Here in Tintagel, people have died from getting caught in it.'

'Why? What does it do?'

'It makes you blind. The sea mist is thick and it rolls in very fast. It hides everything in a white fog and you can't see where you're going. You could fall over the cliff into those dangerous waves, and a cat or a dog could easily be drowned. Or you could lose your way home and go round in endless circles. Look at it, Merlin, how quickly it is coming in over the water.'

I studied the mist and saw that Josephine was right. But I still hadn't told her.

'We must say goodbye.' She stood on tiptoe to kiss me. 'Do you know your way back to Imelda?'

'Yes – no – I don't know,' I said, 'but – wait, I need to tell you something important.' She did wait, gazing at me, sweetly and patiently. So I said it. 'I've fallen in love with you, Josephine. I – I'll love you for all of my life.'

She blinked her golden eyes. 'I love you too, Merlin. You're the best cat I've ever seen. But we must go home, before we get caught in the mist. Make sure you keep walking away from the sea. My home is further along this path, but yours is the other way.' She did a beautiful purr-meow. We kissed and rubbed cheeks. 'Goodbye, Merlin. I'll never forget you. Never.'

'I'll never forget you,' I said. 'I'll keep you in my heart. And I'll be back – one day.'

To say goodbye seemed too final. So I stood breaking my heart as Josephine disappeared into the mist. She moved so lightly, as if the wind was blowing her away.

The mist felt cold. It was all around me now and everything was hidden. The path, the rocks, the clumps of plant life, and the sea and sky. All gone. Invisible. I was cold and bewildered. I'd never experienced mist like this before. Close to panic, I stood still, my tail drooping. I wanted to run after Josephine and go into her home with her, but I couldn't even see which way she had gone.

Afraid to move, I crept back onto the rock that was like an armchair. Josephine's warmth, and mine, was still there on the cushion of sea pinks. I hunkered down and tucked my paws under my body for warmth, and wrapped my tail around myself like a scarf. Surely the mist would go away – wouldn't it?

I waited, and tried to stay happy. I wanted to get back to Imelda, but I wished Josephine could come with me. It had been the best day of my whole life. If only I could stay in the golden bubble of joy I'd shared with Josephine. Her beauty would haunt me for ever. Her perfect grey-and-white coat, the grey on her back and tail, and the white on her breast and tummy, and on her face. Her colour was like a seagull's.

Even as I noticed it, there was a rush of wings and a seagull swooped out of the mist and landed on top of a rock right in front of me. He was very close, too close for comfort. I growled in my throat, like Bully Boy would have done. The big seagull ignored my threat, folded his grey wings and stood motionless, looking at me with one yellow eye.

Why was he looking at me? Surely seagulls didn't eat cats, did they? I watched him, without moving, and he watched me, without moving. He seemed to be listening.

It was getting dark and the mist was drifting, making a glaze of droplets over my fur and on my ears. The sea sounded muffled. Would I have to stay here all night getting colder and colder? The presence of the seagull was surprisingly reassuring. I felt he was deliberately keeping me from moving. I studied him, and a light dawned in my anxious mind. Was it HIM? The seagull who had kept gliding past the window, peering in at me? Convinced it really was him, I changed my attitude and gave him a moderately friendly meow.

The yellow eye registered it, and moments later the great bird stretched his throat, opened his orange beak to the sky and did his screeching, melodic call, on and on, almost turning himself inside out with the effort. Then he tilted his head, listening for a reaction, and it came.

'Merlin. MERLIN.'

Imelda's voice! Calling me. She was out, in the mist, searching for me. How I loved her.

I sat up and considered which kind of meow to do. It had to be my loud, lost-kitten, calling meow, which was almost as loud as the seagull. The yellow eye gave me a blink of approval and I carried on, getting into a rhythm.

Imelda wasn't far away. And she had a bag of fish and chips. I could smell it. I glanced at the seagull and hoped he might get a few chips because I was going to. My spirits lifted when I heard footsteps scuffing along the path. Imelda, and someone else, a man, was with her.

'Stay where you are, Merlin,' she called. 'We're on our way. I can hear you, lovely boy.'

I felt suddenly warm, and passionate, and loved again. Excited, and happy – and starving. I could even hear the paper crackling. She'd got me a hot piece of fish. I knew she had.

A cone of light came bobbing through the mist and a man in a yellow jacket appeared. He shone the powerful torch at me. 'There he is!' he said in a cheerful, friendly voice. I jumped down from the rock with my tail up and ran to Imelda, doing purr-meows. 'Aw, isn't he a beauty,' the man said. 'What a gorgeous cat.'

A nice man, I thought, and noticed some squiggles on his jacket. RNLI. I'd give him a cuddle when I'd finished with Imelda. She cried a bit and tucked me inside her warm parka. 'I've got you back, angel cat.

I love you so much.' I snuggled into her, purring, and when she'd finished kissing me, she opened her bag and fed me morsels of hot, battered fish.

'You are a lucky cat,' said the RNLI man, who was called Seb. 'I wish I had a lovely girl like Imelda to look after me.'

Chapter 13

'Don't Tell Imelda'

'Wow, 'Melda,' Brad said. 'What a transformation! You're like . . . like a butterfly that's just come out of its chrysalis.'

Brad seemed tired but he smiled when he saw Imelda still glowing from the holiday. He couldn't stop glancing at her, as if he'd never seen her before.

Imelda flushed. I knew what she was thinking. She was remembering the moment when the RNLI man, Seb, had spoken so kindly to her. He'd said what a great girl she was, and I'd seen a light come on in her mind. His compliment kindled a life-changing flame for Imelda. I hoped it would never leave her.

'You look pretty,' Brad said.

'You don't,' she teased.

'Don't what?'

'Look pretty.'

Brad grinned and rubbed the stubble on his chin. 'Yeah, sorry. I was going to shave but I haven't had time. How's Merlin?'

'He's fine.' Imelda opened the cat cage and I stepped out, taking care to appear pleased to see Brad. I wove myself round and round his puckered leather boots and frayed jeans, gazing up at him. He needed some cat love. I let him pick me up.

'Don't hold him up in the air, Dad.' Imelda rolled her eyes.

'No, Your Majesty.' Brad grinned and held me nicely, the way Imelda had taught him. 'I never had a cat when I was a boy.' He put me down and picked up Imelda's bag. 'There's a surprise for you inside. In the lounge. Come on in – and you, Sandie. There's something for you too.'

I ran ahead of them with my tail up, through the open front door and into the hall. The house smelled different. It smelled like the vet's surgery. My tail dropped and I felt uneasy. On the stairs was a new chair, fixed to a metal slide, and the house was full of strange energies.

Brad dumped the bag and stood at the lounge door. 'Ta-da! Go and see what's in there, 'Melda.'

I went in with Imelda. She stopped just inside the door and her mouth fell open. She dumped all the stuff she was holding. Even her mobile phone went flying.

'MUM!' she cried, and ran to hug a beautiful, smiling lady who was sitting in Chloe's favourite armchair. 'Aw, Mum, you're home. You're home.'

'Darling!'

There were tears – happy tears, and a hug that went on and on. I sat close and looked majestic. Who was this ethereal person in the pinkest of cardigans with a chiffon scarf covered in tiny gold stars?

'And Merlin. How you have grown! What a lovely cat you are now.' Her voice was quiet and whispery. She held out her hand to me and I tiptoed up to her. She looked too fragile for me to sit on, so I settled on the arm of the chair and did a purr-meow.

Who was she? Suddenly I knew. She was the butterfly who had emerged from a chrysalis called Chloe.

*   *   *

Imelda needed time alone with her mum so I headed out, intending to have a sniff round the garden. Brad and Sandie were leaning on the car, talking about Chloe. Sensing it was important, I sat nearby, innocently washing and discreetly listening. I wanted to know what was going on.

'It was a big decision to bring her home,' Brad said, 'but it's what Chloe wanted. The NHS has arranged a really good care package for her. We couldn't do it without them – I'm out on jobs all day and 'Melda . . . well, it's too much to ask of a child. She's studying for next year's exams, too – it's a vital year for her. I hope she sticks it out.'

'So do I,' Sandie said. 'She's been telling me about her dream of being a vet. It'll be hard work. She has a bad time at school, poor kid, with those bullies. I've told her, Brad, she can come round and talk to me anytime and I'll be there for her. I'm fond of her. She's been no trouble at all and I've enjoyed her company.'

'Thanks,' Brad said in a low, gruff voice. 'I'd better tell you the truth, Sandie, if you don't mind.'

'Yes, do. I won't gossip.'

'Thanks – but please don't speak to Imelda about this. It's better she doesn't know what I'm gonna tell you now.' The tone of his voice spiralled lower and lower. Their faces were serious. 'Chloe had a stroke, as you know, and she's recovering gradually. The physios are marvellous. They're helping her regain the use of her left arm and leg but it's taking time. It's not easy for Chloe because she's always been strong and independent. Imelda knows about the stroke but . . .' Brad took a deep breath and blew his cheeks out. 'The truth is, Sandie . . .'

Sandie listened compassionately. 'Take your time, Brad. Tell me later if it's hard to say.'

'No. I must tell you.' He fidgeted and kept blinking and staring at the sky. Finally he managed to meet Sandie's eyes. 'Chloe has got cancer. I'm gutted. Just gutted. She's taking the news better than me.'

'Oh no, I'm so sorry, Brad.'

More deep breaths. Then Brad continued, 'I won't go into the details, but it's inoperable and it's metas- tasized. They talked us through the options. To put her through chemo and radiotherapy when she's still recovering from the stroke would be too much for her. Chloe knows and understands and, to be honest, she's acting so calm and down to earth. I never knew she could be that courageous.'

Sandie was shaking her head. She could hardly speak, except to offer crumbs of compassion, like, 'Poor Chloe,' and then, 'Poor Imelda. How's she going to cope? Is it . . . is it terminal?'

Brad nodded. He crumpled a bit more each time he explained about Chloe's condition. 'I'm afraid so. That's what they've told us. Six months to a year she's got. She opted for palliative care and she wanted to come home. But we both agreed Imelda must not be told. Maybe nearer the time, but not now.'

'Thank goodness she's got Merlin,' Sandie said. I stopped washing and gave her my full attention. 'Animals understand more than we think they do and Merlin's a highly intelligent cat. Aren't you, Merlin?'

I did a yes-meow and ran to Sandie. She smoothed my fur. 'No, I'm not going to pick you up,' she said, and turned back to Brad. 'I'll come in and see Chloe for a minute,' she said, 'then I want to get home and get meself sorted out.'

'And we're giving you a bottle of wine,' Brad said, 'as a thank you.'

As they went into the house a cloud of depression and anxiety suddenly engulfed me. Their words hung in the air. How was I going to help Imelda to cope?

* * *

With Chloe at home, our life became very different. Chloe could hardly walk and she needed a lot of care. She didn't sit at her table and work any more; instead of bills and papers, the table had flowers in jars and pretty cards. I made a huge effort not to play with them. We all made sacrifices for Chloe. Brad didn't want to go to work, but he did; Imelda feared and hated school, but she managed to go just to keep her mother happy.

Every morning I was in charge of the house and it was my job to welcome the carers who came to help Chloe. They were the loveliest people I'd ever met and they brought cheerful voices, laughter and encouragement into our home. The walls rang with their kindness. There was Pierre, a solemn-eyed French nurse. Cathy, a beaming, grey-haired lady who worked like mad and dispensed crumbs of wisdom with the medication. And Annalise, who was a Marie Curie nurse, quiet and serene. I loved all three of them and it wasn't long before they loved me, and Annalise even brought me 'cat treats' and little toys. She fixed a sun-catcher crystal in the window and I had fun trying the catch the rainbows it made.

Laughter was good for Imelda, and I discovered that sometimes the best way to make her relax was to play. At other times, she was so overwhelmed and tired that all I could do was cuddle up to her and gaze into her eyes.

Outside in the garden, the autumn glowed with scarlet berries, and flame-coloured leaves blew in shoals across the lawn. I had a brilliant time playing with them, charging into heaps, leaping in the air to catch them and actually frightening myself with the furious rustling sounds I was making.

Early mornings were misty and magical and I enjoyed being out in the garden where I would sit watching the spiders on their dew-spangled cobwebs. The swallows were long gone – gone to Africa, Imelda told me. A different gang of birds ruled the skies – vast flocks of starlings who made swerving patterns high in the air.

I relied on Bully Boy to explain about the seasonal changes. The leaves falling. The dark evenings. The rain and the frost. It was all new to me. He did warn me about one particular time when cats were in great danger. It went on for days, or even weeks, he said, and it was something dreadful which humans did. They lit enormous bonfires and sent sparkly things whooshing into the night sky where they would explode. The bangs shook and terrified every living creature, and sometimes killed them. Even Bully Boy was scared and he went miles into the woods to a special den he'd made under a bramble thicket. He invited me to go with him, if I needed to feel safe.

Imelda was nervous about this event, which she called 'Fireworks Night'. When the first bangs happened in our road, she wanted to shut me in, and for a few nights it was OK. It was raining and I didn't want to go out anyway. I enjoyed the lovely warm fire we had in the lounge, and the luxury of stretching out on the rug and warming my belly.

Chloe really liked me now and I gave her lots of love and purring. She spent her time reading or helping Imelda with homework. The two of them would stare at the laptop or at books while I rolled on the rug in the amazing heat from the fire. How I longed to bring Bully Boy inside on a cold November night and let him experience the therapy of a real log fire. But he wouldn't go in a house.

Some nights, Imelda had to put her mum to bed and it took ages. Helping her on to the stairlift, and then getting her undressed and into bed should have been simple, but it wasn't. Imelda tried to be patient. She tried so hard. But many nights, she cried to me about it and I made sure I was waiting for her when she finally came to bed. Chloe sometimes called out for help in the night and it was always Imelda, and not Brad, who woke up and spent a long time seeing to Chloe's complex needs. Neither of us slept, except on the nights when Annalise came and quietly stayed beside Chloe all night long.

We were just about managing – until, one starry, frosty night, the terrible fireworks began.

Chapter 14

Fireworks Night

'For goodness' sake, pull yourself together, girl.' Brad was exasperated with Imelda, who had come home from school crying. He pushed her into the kitchen and shut the door. I was in there eating my tea peacefully.

'Get off me, Dad. You've no right to push me around,' Imelda sobbed with fury.

'I shouldn't have to,' Brad said. 'We can't have you kicking off when your mum is so ill. Stop howling like a five-year-old and get a hold of yourself.'

'But you don't understand, and you won't listen. I had a firework thrown at me when I got off the school bus. How would you like it?'

'Did it burn you? Did it?'

'No.'

'Well, stop making such a fuss. Boys will do these stupid things. Take no notice of them. It's Fireworks Night.'

'You just don't care, do you?' Imelda went on crying furiously.

'Will you SHUT UP?' Brad's face flushed and his eyes bulged. 'We don't want your mum to hear you.'

'Oh, so I could break my heart, or drop dead, as long as SHE doesn't hear me.'

''Melda, your mum's not well today.'

'I do know that. Who gets up and helps her three times a night? Not you. Me. Good old Imelda, every time. I don't get proper sleep, and I'm really stressed over the fireworks.'

'So what's new? You've been stressing over fireworks for the entire week. I know you're worried about Merlin – so keep him in.'

I looked up at Brad in alarm. Those words! Keep him in. Keep him in. Hadn't I heard them all through our week in Tintagel? I didn't want to be kept in.

'It's not that simple, Dad.'

'Why not? You make more fuss over that cat than you do over your mum.'

'It's too much for me. I just want to go to bed and catch up on sleep. I can't possibly do all the things you expect of me, and face the bullies at school,

AND study for my exams.' Imelda was trembling with fury.

I left my tea half-eaten and ran to her. I sat gazing up at her but she didn't pick me up. *That firework,* I thought, *it didn't burn her body. It burned her soul.* I jumped on to the kitchen worktop and stretched out my paw to touch her. But she seemed blind and deaf, unable to respond.

'Get OFF the worktop, cat!' Brad clapped his big, dusty hands at me. Miffed, I jumped down and did my plea-from-the-heart meow. I was desperate to help Imelda. I could calm her down. Why wasn't she seeing me? Had she gone beyond the point of no return?

'And YOU' – Brad jerked his thumb at Imelda – 'get your school uniform off and start cooking our tea. This is real life, not a soap opera.'

'No, I will not – and you can't make me. I'm going to bed.' Imelda slammed out of the kitchen door and up the stairs, ignoring my second attempt at a plea-from-the-heart meow.

Brad wasn't angry. He looked beaten and unloved. For a moment, we stood in the kitchen and stared at each other, shocked . . . and powerless.

Imelda had forgotten me. Brad had called me 'that cat' when I was trying to help.

'It's Fireworks Night. We've got to keep you in, cat.'

CAT! Me? I was Merlin. Wasn't I?

And he'd said those words again. *Keep you in.*

Brad picked up the roll of sticky tape, and I made a quick decision. He was going to tape the cat flap to stop me going out. I threw him a glare of contempt and challenge. If I couldn't help Imelda and Brad wasn't listening, then my place wasn't here tonight. I took off as if my paws were on fire. I slammed out of the cat flap and sped across the garden, crossed a road in full flight and headed down the alleyway with my tail flying.

One of the gardens that backed on to the alleyway was full of excited people. Bundled in scarves and bobble hats, they were clustered around a high pyramid of junk – mostly broken wood. I wasn't stopping for anything but I did notice something weird on top of the pyramid – a man made of sticks dressed in shabby old clothes, his bottle-top eyes glaring out from under a straw hat.

I sped on, down the long alleyway. The air was glazed with frost but smoky with the fumes of barbecues and the smell of sausages and pickle. I heard a few random bangs but I ignored them. Bully Boy had done a good job of explaining Fireworks Night to me. His overriding message was: get to your safe place before dark and stay there until morning. He'd invited me to join him in his secret den. But was I too late?

With a knot of fear in my mind, I charged along the lane and under the wrought-iron gates, where I paused to calm my breathing: I'd made it into the wild wood. Phew!

I had no idea where Bully Boy's Fireworks Night den was so I chose to climb, once again, into the beech tree. The hollow between the branches was still there and not occupied. Pleased, I settled in to the deep nest of crunchy leaves. It was warm, as if summer had gone to sleep in every leaf that had been blown from the trees. I gazed in awe at the bare twigs against the sky, and realised the great beech tree was asleep. Yet it still held me, effortlessly, and I felt safe.

But when I smelled the smoke from the big bonfire, I was worried. Was I too close? Should I dash through the darkening woods and try to find Bully Boy? With him beside me, I would be safe.

The crackle of the flames was loud and fierce. The glow coloured the sky. Enormous red sparks zig-zagged in the windblown smoke. I tried not to be afraid, but I was. Why was I out here when I could have been purring in Imelda's bed? What kind of crazy decision had I made? I crouched in the nest of leaves, making myself smaller and smaller. If only Bully Boy would come, but he didn't. There was no sign of him.

Without warning, the fireworks began. It was like the end of the world. They weren't tiny little bangs like a balloon bursting. Each bang was a monumental thump which sent a shockwave right through me. I dug my claws into the bark and hung on. The trees in the wild wood were sleeping giants and yet the shockwaves passed through them. I felt it in my sensitive paws. Between bangs, the wild wood rustled with panicking, fleeing rabbits, badgers and deer. Blackbirds who had gone to roost were waking up again, flying in the dark, their alarm calls urgent and terrified. I thought about the tiny creatures who lived in the wild wood and in the surrounding gardens. The bees, the moths and dragonflies. Were they, like me, awake and afraid, compelled to watch the great flowers of light in the sky, and to suffer the harmful vibration of each reverberating boom?

Had it been only a few bangs, I might have coped. But there were more and more, tumbling over each other. They hurt my delicate ears with a sharp, ringing pain. I didn't think I could stand it.

Imelda would have explained it to me. I was missing her already, and wanted to go back. But I heeded

Bully Boy's advice. Hide in a safe place and stay there until morning. In the morning, it would be quiet.

Fountains of light filled the sky and I had no way of understanding what they were. To a lonely little cat, the incredible lights were apocalyptic. I really believed the sun, moon and stars were flying apart, and it would be the end of the world, even for cats.

I was determined to survive but it went on for hour after punishing hour. My head ached as if it was screaming inside. It hurt so badly that I felt I might go berserk and run around crashing into things. Or I would run for miles in search of silence. Healing, beautiful silence.

Fireworks Night.

It had broken me.

I was still a ginger cat.

A cat in terrible pain.

I prayed for help.

Eventually the noises stopped, but I was too scared to leave my safe place. I wondered if Imelda was as scared as me and wished I'd stayed with her. It took a long time, but finally I slept, and when I awoke there was only the deep quiet of the wild wood. In the night, I had sunk deeper into the nest of leaves and built up some warmth by keeping my paws tucked under and my tail wrapped around me. Only my back, nose and ears were cold. The leaf nest had effectively insulated me. I wasn't a cat. I was a mound of dry leaves with a little cat face, pink nose and white whiskers surfacing as if I were swimming.

I blinked my emerald eyes and raised my head to gaze at an enchanted woodland of glistening frost. The fireworks had not destroyed the whole world. In the twilight before dawn, everything was glazed in hoar frost. The beech twigs, the domes of moss, the cobwebs. All frozen into silence.

The only sound was a robin singing. We saw each other and I didn't want to catch him. I was glad of his company.

*   *   *

Bully Boy didn't appear. I guessed he was snuggled into his den, like me, reluctant to step out into the cold air. Thank goodness Fireworks Night was over. I could go home and creep under the duvet. Imelda would soon be waking up and missing me.

The thought of her brought a rush of anxiety and guilt. The enormity of what I had done hit me hard. I'd abandoned her! When she most needed me. I was ashamed.

While I was experiencing these painful emotions, the robin dared to come closer to me. He sat on a nearby twig, eyeing me and cranking up his little song, making it louder, faster. I paid attention. Bully Boy had told me how robins were messengers, how they knew everything that was going on and didn't hesitate to tell you. Never kill a robin, he'd said. Even if he was starving, he wouldn't kill one.

The rising sun wheeled its perfectly straight rays between the branches. It was time for me to go home. The hidden creatures of the wood and the spirits of the wood seemed to be shouting at me. Go home. GO HOME.

It was hard to climb out of the warm nest, my legs stiff from being locked in sleep, my spine tense from the anxiety and pain of Fireworks Night. I needed to roll on the rug in front of the fire.

I hurried home along the familiar route, past the charred remains of the bonfire, the air still thick with acrid whiffs of smoke. I was glad to reach the wall of our garden. I fluffed my fur, put my tail up and dashed around the side of the house to the cat flap. I hesitated, hearing voices in the drive at the front door. I trotted round there eagerly. Perhaps I'd see Imelda on her way out to school and we'd have a cuddle. She'd forgive me for abandoning her and she'd be happy to find I'd survived Fireworks Night.

But what I saw chilled me to the bone and filled me with dread. Outside our home was a police car with its blue light flashing. Brad was at the front door, white-faced, staring at the policeman and policewoman who stood there. The policeman was holding Imelda's bike helmet. 'This probably saved her life,' he said, 'but she is still very seriously injured. She has a badly broken leg, and possibly spinal injuries.'

'Try not to worry,' the policewoman said. 'I know the team at our hospital and they are extraordinary. Imelda is in very good hands.'

Brad took the bike helmet from the policeman and stood holding it with both hands, cold with shock but hot with anger. His knees shook but his eyes glittered with fury. He started swearing and calling Imelda names.

'Try to calm yourself, sir.' The policeman put a kindly hand on Brad's shoulder. 'This is your daughter we're talking about, isn't it? Imelda?'

'I TOLD her not to go,' Brad ranted, 'but she ignored me, as usual. That girl's been trouble, trouble, TROUBLE, since the day she was born. And she's been worse since we had that cat. Obsessed with him, she is. Just because he went missing last night – what with the fireworks going on – she had to go out on her bike this morning, in the rush-hour traffic. Madness. She wouldn't have been looking where she was going.'

'It wasn't actually her fault,' the policeman said. 'The car swerved to avoid some idiot who was overtaking in the other direction.'

Brad held Imelda's helmet tightly against his body and I could see it shaking. He was shattered and scared, that was clear. Would this be the moment for me to swan in with my tail up? I'd gaze at him and be a kind, loving cat. Surely I could calm him down.

I wondered where Imelda was. She'd be pleased to see me.

I followed them inside into the lounge where Annalise was settling Chloe into her armchair. Chloe's eyes widened in horror when she saw the police coming in. I sat in the doorway thinking I might need to escape. My tail twitched anxiously. What was happening?

'My wife is ill,' Brad mumbled, 'as you can see.' He took the bike helmet over to Chloe and put it into her frail hands. 'It . . . it's our 'Melda,' he sobbed, and collapsed in the chair next to her. Then he couldn't speak at all but sat, hunched, taking deep breaths.

I was afraid to go to him. He'd call me 'that cat' and push me away. I wanted Imelda. Where was she?

I listened carefully to the talking, trying to understand. Feelings of shock and grief criss-crossed the room. It was not the time for a grand entrance with my tail up. I sidled in, approaching Chloe gently, and leaned against her legs, giving a soft purr-meow. I'm here, I wanted to say. I'm here for you.

Chloe let me climb on to her lap and purr. She stroked me without seeing me. Her thin body was quivering. Even the floorboards under the carpet were trembling with the shockwaves coming from Brad and Chloe.

'My poor, poor little girl,' Chloe said, her voice suddenly strong with compassion. 'We must go to the hospital, immediately.'

Brad shook his head. 'You can't, Chloe,'

'I CAN,' Chloe said firmly. 'You get the car out and I'll be ready. Take my wheelchair.'

'I wouldn't drive, sir, until you've had a chance to calm down,' the policeman said to Brad.

'We'll get a taxi,' Chloe said. 'I must be with her.'

'We can't afford a taxi.' Brad's shaky spell was quickly turning to resentment. 'Anyway, I'm not going. I'm too angry with her. It's her own silly fault.'

Chloe sent him an icy, pitying look. 'Is that the message you'd like me to give our badly injured daughter?'

'No,' Brad growled. He stood up. 'I'd best get to work if we're gonna be paying for taxis.'

He nodded at the policeman and walked out, dumping Imelda's helmet on the sofa. My heart went out to Chloe, so fragile and upset.

Annalise spoke out as soon as Brad had gone. 'I'll take you, dear Chloe. It's no trouble and you need someone with you.'

'Thanks.' Chloe saw me. 'Merlin doesn't understand what's going on. Would you feed him, Annalise, before we go?'

I followed Annalise into the kitchen while the police said goodbye to Chloe.

'I'll be back later, with Chloe,' Annalise told me, 'but Imelda won't be home for a while, Merlin. You're going to miss her.'

I listened, but didn't understand. Still shocked from the fireworks, I bounded upstairs, half-expecting Imelda to be there, but she wasn't. I crawled under the duvet and lay in the place where her heart would usually be.

I told myself Imelda would soon come home, perhaps tomorrow. I'd be here, waiting for her.

Chapter 15

Love, Like Never Before

Imelda was gone. How could I live without her? Day and night, I stayed on her bed. I didn't play, eat or drink but just lay there, grieving, not caring about anything. I didn't understand where Imelda was. 'Hospital' was a strange word for me. Chloe had tried to explain. She'd told me Imelda was in bed – but she wasn't. I was spending lonely nights on her bed, hoping she would soon be back. Brad popped his head round the door during my vigil, only once, and he didn't stroke me or try to be kind. He said something awful to me: 'You needn't think you can stay there for ever, cat.' I got the message. I knew that when Brad called me 'cat', he didn't want me. I was even more upset.

The following morning when Brad had gone to work, Annalise, the Marie Curie nurse, came in to see me. I liked and trusted her but I didn't lift my head or purr. I couldn't even look at her. She sat on the bed and smoothed my fur. 'I'm checking to see if you are hurt, Merlin,' she said in her sweet, quiet voice, and she ran her hands over my back and tummy. She examined each one of my paws, inspected my pads and my tail. She wrapped her hands around my ribs to see if my breathing was OK. I let her gently open my mouth and peer inside.

'You are all right, Merlin,' she said, 'but you're broken-hearted, darling. I can see that.'

I was grateful for her attention. To my surprise, Annalise picked me up. I didn't purr or cuddle her. Thoroughly depressed, I leaned against her like a rag doll, not caring. 'Chloe wants to see you, darling,' she said, and carried me downstairs and into the lounge.

Chloe was in a chair by the window. Her clothes were beautiful colours but her skin seemed almost transparent, pale as the moon, and she was so thin and worried. But she was nothing like the old Chloe, who had been frowning and angry. She looked ethereal and wise.

'Would you like to hold Merlin?' Annalise asked, and Chloe nodded eagerly. She held out her good arm and Annalise lowered me on to her lap, which was covered by a soft blanket.

'Merlin.' Chloe said my name lovingly, and it made a difference to the way I felt. 'I've never seen you like this,' she said in deep concern.

'I've checked him over,' Annalise said, sitting close on a stool. 'He's not injured in any way that I can see – but I think he's in shock. Maybe the fireworks scared him.'

Chloe stroked me in a soothing rhythm. It felt good. 'Normally he'd be purring,' she said, and then spoke directly to me, looking into my eyes. 'Did those fireworks upset you?'

I managed a subdued, monosyllabic meow.

'It's a terrible night for animals,' Annalise said. 'I've got a cat and a dog, and they hated it. My dog crawled on his belly under the table and he was shivering and so distressed.'

Chloe kept on steadily looking into my eyes. 'Is it Imelda you're worrying about, Merlin?'

This time, I did a meow which turned into a cry, and it went on and on until I had no breath.

The two women exchanged glances.

'Do you want to know what's happened?' Chloe asked me, and I let out another plaintive meow.

Chloe was surprisingly kind. She stroked my face and rubbed behind my ears and under my chin while she explained. 'Imelda loves you very much, Merlin, and she was terrified when you disappeared on Fireworks Night. She thought you'd get hurt or frightened. She stayed awake all night and she was really tired. Oh, I wish I'd noticed how stressed she was.' Tears ran down Chloe's thin cheeks. 'She went off on her bike early in the morning to try to find you. Brad tried to stop her but she was determined to go. I admire her, really. But . . .' Chloe took a deep breath. 'She was unlucky, poor girl. A car knocked her off her bike about a mile from home and hurt her – a lot. She's got a broken pelvis and a badly broken leg – very bad. She'll have to stay in hospital for a long time, like I did. Are you listening, Merlin? It wasn't your fault, darling cat. You've been such a wonderful friend to her – and to me.'

I listened in amazement, getting the tone and the emotion she was sharing. She looked at Annalise. 'How can I make him understand?'

'He does,' Annalise said. 'Animals do understand. We don't talk to them enough. Just keep telling him.'

So Chloe repeated her words, and I paid attention. I did understand and it was good for me to hear the kindness in her voice. 'Imelda will get better,' she continued. 'The clever doctors and nurses have saved her leg with some complicated surgery – now she needs rest and lots of physiotherapy. She won't be able to walk for a while and so she can't come home yet. But you'll be OK. Have you got that, Merlin?'

'His face is brighter already,' Annalise said. 'Shall I feed him?'

'Not just yet,' Chloe said. 'I want to reassure him if I can. Is it working, Merlin? I wish I knew how to heal you.'

This time, I managed a proper purr-meow. Chloe, who used to be so stressed and angry, wanted to know how to heal? And heal me?

'You do know how to heal,' Annalise said. 'You're doing it right now, Chloe.'

'Am I?' Chloe was surprised.

'It's in the tone of your voice and the touch of your hand and the love you're giving him. He's soaking it up.'

Her encouragement intensified Chloe's touch. She leaned over me and whispered, 'I'm sorry, Merlin, for the times I was angry with you when you were so little. Please forgive me.'

I still couldn't purr but I stretched my front paws over her heart.

'I wish I'd been kinder to Imelda too,' Chloe said. 'She tried so hard, Annalise, to help me. She got up, night after night, and took me to the bathroom, washed me, made me drinks. Even the little things she did were lovely, like putting a drop of lavender oil on my pillow. I should have realised she was getting overtired, and bottling up her worries.' Chloe sighed deeply. 'She's been obsessed for ages with making friends with a dreadful feral cat who's always hanging about the garden. She's been so patient and gentle with it. She told me about this time, when I was in hospital, that she finally managed to get close and stroke this cat. It was a kind of magical experience for her. But Brad was furious with her. It . . . it completely crushed her.'

Balanced on the uncomfortable stool, Annalise listened, her eyes wide and shining with compassion.

Chloe couldn't seem to stop talking. Words poured out of her, on and on, until she reached the hardest thing she wanted to say. More tears flowed and she finally let go of the big worry. 'What will happen, Annalise? What will happen to Imelda when . . . when I'm gone? She can't live with Brad – it would destroy her. He'll have to sell the house and find a little flat. It's not fair on a teenage girl, with all her life in front of her. He wouldn't even let her keep Merlin. He told me that. He said . . . he said, "That cat will have to go."'

I couldn't take it any more. I closed my eyes and let the shock race through me. I needed to go back to my sanctuary on Imelda's bed. But something made me stay there on Chloe's lap.

'And . . .' Chloe had one more worry to share, 'it's not going to be long, is it, Annalise? I'm not going to see Christmas. Am I?'

'Nobody knows,' Annalise said. 'We can only go one day at a time, even one hour at a time. But I'm here – I'll be here for you, dear Chloe. Come on, darling, don't give up. I'm going to take you to see Imelda this afternoon and she really needs you.'

'Thanks.'

Chloe was settling down, breathing steadily again. She'd unloaded her deepest fears.

'Shall I feed you now, Merlin?' Annalise asked. 'You're looking a bit better, aren't you?'

I got down and stretched. It felt good to follow Annalise into the kitchen with my tail up.

But something made me turn and stare back at Chloe. It was an invisible hand turning me, wanting me to witness the brilliance of the light around Chloe. It didn't come from the sun. It was silvery white and luminous.

I sat down, neat and majestic, with my front paws together, watching, welcoming the radiance. To me, it was a friend, the light from the shining lands. It came with a song so high-pitched, like the voices of dolphins, and audible only to me. I was glad to be a cat. I waited and slowly the light flowed out to me and brushed its energy through my fur. I remembered I had been a shining cat. I could never die but only transform. And I remembered how to see with the eyes of a shining cat. How to see with my soul.

I wasn't disappointed. Within the light were two angels, one each side of Chloe. Loving her. And loving me. Giving me back my joy.

Rejuvenated, I turned and walked into the kitchen with a tail so tall that Annalise smiled at me in delight. 'You're all fluffed up like a feather duster, Merlin!' she said.

* * *

I continued to sleep, alone, in Imelda's bed. It was where I felt close to her. I didn't know where she was, despite Chloe telling me she was in hospital. I couldn't imagine where 'hospital' was or what it was. I assumed she would be back one day and, oh, how I'd welcome her. I thought of ways to make her laugh, and planned how beautifully I would purr, how we'd sleep together, contented, knowing we were loved and not alone.

Sometimes I sat on the King Arthur book, which she'd left by the bed, and remembered the stories in there – especially the one I loved most, about the ship of light and the nine big waves bringing a baby boy to Merlin's feet. I dreamed of Tintagel and the day I'd fallen in love with Josephine. Her sweet grey-and-white face was in my heart for ever. We'd go back one day, Imelda had promised. *'We might even live there,'* she'd whispered. Her pink-and-grey backpack was still hidden under the bed, stuffed with the things we'd take to Tintagel. I went under there and played with it and undid the zips but managed to resist taking things out.

For a few days, I didn't venture beyond the garden. I wanted to be sure the fireworks wouldn't come again.

At the end of the garden was a silver birch tree. It was bright and airy and its foliage had turned to gold. The wind streamed through it, sending leaves flying like paper hearts, flickering over green grass. I hurried down to it and climbed up to sit on the widest branch. A good place for a cat to meditate.

My paws felt heavy. My tail drooped. If cats could cry I'd have cried for my humans. Were they for ever lost in a thick fog of problems? Were humans all over the earth like that? Was it because they didn't have fur? I couldn't think of any other creature who had only skin, like a human. No wonder they needed clothes. And houses. And cars. And roads to put them on. And stuff to put inside them. All because of skin!

I imagined what Imelda would be like if she had fur. She'd be draped in a tree, like me. I imagined Brad trying to live in a hollow tree, as Bully Boy did. What would he do with all his stuff? That brought me to another issue. STUFF. Humans spent most of their time organising their stuff. Cleaning it, bundling it into boxes and bags. Then bundling it out again. Arguing over it, especially if it was paper. Paper which cats weren't allowed to play with. I imagined a howling wind invading our house and blowing white flocks of paper out into the sky like birds.

My thoughts turned to my own needs. Had I got any STUFF? I had a catnip mouse. I had a bed I didn't sleep in, and a collar I didn't like. Cats don't need stuff. The liberating truth illuminated my meditation in the birch tree. The only piece of stuff I would have was a mobile phone. To me, Imelda's 'smartphone' was a tablet of limitless telepathy.

Oh, and the other piece of stuff I'd have would be Imelda's bed. To me, it was a delectable marshmallow of softness and comfort. Fifty cats could have slept in it.

I sighed, and opened my eyes to see the sunlight and the wind streaming through the birch tree. I felt better. Lighter, more fluffy, and more alive. My 'cat meditation' had lifted me out of the gloom. My angel hadn't spoken but I felt energised and free. I glanced at the sky and saw the shimmering edge of a wing, slipping away into the clouds.

I was ready to go indoors, reconnect with Chloe, and run upstairs to rediscover Imelda's bed.

* * *

One afternoon when I was sitting on the King Arthur book, I heard Sandie coming upstairs. 'Where are you, Merlin?'

I meowed to her. She came in wearing a heavy coat with a bright scarf. It was a surprise when she picked me up and carried me downstairs, holding me firmly. Brad was waiting in the kitchen with my travelling basket open. It was a trick. I struggled but Sandie deftly and quickly put me inside and, before I could turn around, Brad had fastened the catch.

What was happening? Was I going to the vet? I wailed to be let out. Why hadn't I been smart enough to reverse out of the basket and run away?

'Are you sure you can manage him, Sandie? You'll have to carry him a long way down all those corridors.'

'Course I can manage him.' Sandie looked in at me. 'Don't you worry, Merlin, I'm taking you in my car and we're going to see Imelda. Have you got that?'

'No,' I meowed.

'So settle down and behave.' Sandie carried my cage outside and put it in the car. I stared out at the garden and Bully Boy was on the wall! I hadn't seen him for weeks and I really needed to be with him. I kicked up a fuss, yowling and scrabbling.

'For goodness' sake,' Sandie said. 'You're not on fire.'

But I was on fire. On fire with the irony of it. I'd longed to see Bully Boy. What would he think? Sandie didn't care. She started the car and we went whizzing off into the traffic. I didn't like Sandie's style of driving. She drove like a blue tit, stopping and starting and pecking at traffic lights.

Frustrated, I started excavating the cushion, got it open and ripped out great wads of white stuffing.

'Here we are. This is the hospital.'

I stopped attacking the cushion and peered out, telling myself it was a good idea to see a hospital and know what it was like. Perhaps I could then search for Imelda. We pulled in to a car park in front of a towering glass building, its windows reflecting a sky of racing clouds.

Sandie tutted at the shredded cushion. She spoke sharply to me. 'Now, you calm down, lovely boy, or I won't take you in to see Imelda. She's in bed and she's not very well. So you behave. None of that yowling.'

My cage bounced up and down as Sandie marched into the glass building. I tried to be quiet but it was scary, especially the lift. Sandie was very determined and she talked her way past the reception desk. Eventually a nurse ushered us into a small room, closing the door firmly behind us and standing with her back to it, as if on guard.

There was a high bed in the room, and there, lying in it, was Imelda! But there was something wrong. She lay on her side staring at the wall. She didn't move, even when Sandie spoke to her. 'Hi, Imelda. It's Sandie, and look who I've brought to see you.'

There was no response – except from my angel who unexpectedly filled the small hospital room with a whoosh of shimmering light. She whispered to me when I was still in the cage. 'Merlin! Merlin, today, you must give Imelda everything. Your best, best love. Your warmth. Your healing paws. Hold nothing back. Give everything.'

Sandie let me out of the cage. I was overwhelmed by a rush of love. I fluffed my fur and jumped on to the bed with my tail up. I did my best purr-meow and walked up the mound of Imelda's body. I peeped over at her face and purred like I'd never purred before.

I wrapped my paws around her neck, loving her like never before. Waiting and praying for a response. It didn't take long. My love at last made Imelda smile and look more like herself. She even giggled when my whiskers brushed her cheek. 'Aw, Merlin, you're wonderful. What would I do without you?'

As I lay there close to her, I remembered the games we loved to play at home. Imelda would move her hand or her toe under the duvet and I'd pounce on it. We'd pretend it was a mouse. She thought my antics were hilarious and the more she laughed, the more I did it. What if I tried it now?

The hospital bed was covered in a thin cellular blanket, and it wasn't long before I saw Imelda's toes wiggling. A spark of mischief gleamed in her eyes, so I pranced down the bed and pounced. She laughed, and so did Sandie.

Even the nurse laughed at me. 'What a wonderful cat!' she said. 'He's doing Imelda a power of good.'

Imelda gave Sandie a hug too. 'Thanks, Sandie, for bringing him in. I really appreciate it. You've been so kind to me – like a fairy godmother.'

Sandie chuckled. 'Me? Some fairy! But you're welcome, Imelda dear. I think the world of you – and . . . if things get tough, you can come and stay over with me, like you used to when you were little. And Merlin can come. So don't you worry. You relax and get better and do everything the physiotherapists tell you.'

'Thanks.' Imelda put her hands on each side of my face and spoke to me. 'Now, I'd love you to stay here with me, Merlin, but you can't. You go home with Sandie and be a good cat – and one day I'll come home, and we might even go to Tintagel again.'

I didn't want to leave Imelda. I crawled under the blanket and cuddled close to her. I licked her soft cheek and patted her hair. We gazed at each other.

'Come on, Merlin.' Sandie had to lift me out. She gently unhooked my claws as I tried to cling to Imelda.

At least I knew where she was, and I understood that she couldn't walk.

Sandie kept asking me to be good, and I tried, but the parting was a moment of heartbreak for me, and for Imelda.

Chapter 16

The Night the Angels Came

My life changed for ever on the night the angels came for Chloe.

She was upstairs in bed, with Brad and Annalise one each side of her. The house brooded and a glaze of anxiety clung to the walls. The hall clock ticked like a frightened heart. My paws made soft thuds on the stairs and along the landing.

Chloe needed me. The last thing I could do for her was purr. Her voice was weak, as if it was coming from the moon. 'Let him stay,' she whispered, and I settled down with extreme gentleness and care on the cool, silky quilt close to her heart. Chloe was frail and could hardly move but she wanted to stroke me, so Annalise lifted her limp hand and placed it on my fur. I purred deeply, rhythmically, for her to feel the vibration of my love.

'It's comforting her,' Annalise whispered to Brad, who had enveloped Chloe's other hand in his own, his head bowed as if he were praying.

Chloe struggled to say something, her voice so quiet that Annalise leaned over to listen. 'You want the curtains open, dear? Of course.' Annalise went to the window and drew the dark curtains back. A square of brilliant night sky shone in and Chloe turned her face to the stars and smiled.

I felt like part of a team as Brad, Annalise and I kept watch over Chloe. Her last words glimmered like precious gems in the silence. 'Thank you,' she said. 'Thank you for loving me.' I knew from her touch on my fur that I was included. She paused and I glanced at Brad who was completely still, his silent tears shining in the starlight as they dripped on to the quilt.

Chloe's eyes were only half-open but she turned them to me. 'Darling Merlin,' she murmured, 'look after my Imelda. She's in . . . in my heart. Always.'

She let her eyes close. Her breathing changed, becoming shallow and spaced out, each breath further and further apart. I kept on steadily purring, aware of its simple power to calm and comfort.

Nobody spoke. We held on to Chloe and sent her love, and waited. Another breath. And another. The bright stars shining in.

I sensed the angels coming and stopped purring. I lifted my head and felt the wind from their wings, heard the high-frequency music from the shining lands. I gazed in awe as the two angels filled the room, the house and the world beyond with their shimmering light. Was I going with them? Would they take me? No, I must stay. I must go on, waiting for Imelda, still loving her wherever she was, believing that one day we would meet again.

I am only a ginger cat. But I watched as Chloe went so gently, her spirit face radiant with incredulous joy. She held out her arms and let the angels take her, the three of them disappearing with the grace of a thistle seed being blown for miles across the golden meadows of summer.

* * *

I didn't grieve for Chloe. I grieved for Imelda. I needed to know when she'd be coming home from hospital.

It was raining so I spent the morning sleeping in Imelda's bed, trying to feel close to her. The house was busy all day with strange visitors talking to Brad. Annalise stayed there, offering a quiet, supportive presence and making endless cups of coffee. Heavy footsteps plodded up and down the stairs, and I heard them carrying Chloe's body and loading it into a big black car.

When all was quiet, Annalise came into Imelda's bedroom to say goodbye to me. She picked me up and sat on the bed with me. 'I won't be coming here any more, Merlin,' she said, 'but you'll be all right, dear cat. Brad will be here to look after you, won't he?'

My eyes must have shown my unease, and I felt sad and tense. Brad – looking after me? Annalise, not coming any more? It sounded bleak.

I trusted Annalise so there was no need to pretend I was OK when I wasn't. I stared at her kind face and did my plea-from-the-heart meow.

'What's the matter?' she asked immediately, so I did another one, even longer and louder. She stroked me lovingly and tried to explain where Imelda was. 'I know you miss her, sweetheart, and I'll bet she misses you.'

I leaned against her and I wasn't purring. Annalise held me lovingly and patiently told me again about Imelda several times, but I couldn't take the words in. Then she said, 'I'm a Marie Curie nurse, Merlin, and my job is to look after people when they are dying. So tomorrow I'll be going to another family, across town, to care for their grandad.'

I tried to understand but a sense of desolation was building in my mind. I was being abandoned. By everyone. And I imagined Imelda felt the same.

*　*　*

Later that day when it was getting dark, Brad came into Imelda's bedroom with two big bags. I was sitting in the window, on the King Arthur book. 'This has got to be done,' he mumbled. 'Imelda's out of hospital. She's going to be in a rehabilitation unit for a few months, somewhere far away where she'll get fit and healthy again. I'm selling this house. Can't afford to live here now.'

Out of hospital? But where had she gone? I wished then that I'd listened more carefully to Annalise's explanations. Bewildered and horrified, I watched him stripping Imelda's bed, folding up everything – even the pillowcases – until only the mattress and the bare pillows were left. He took her laptop, wound the cable around it and stuffed it into a bag. He opened the wardrobe and took out some of her jeans and tops, trying to fold them but getting increasingly impatient as he bundled them into the bag. Shoes, scarves and underwear went in, then he chose some teddy bears from the shelf – and the fluffy dolphin – and crammed everything in, grumbling and sighing about 'how much STUFF' she had.

He cleared the bedside table. Then he opened the top drawer, took it out and emptied the entire contents into the bag in a jingling heap. With both bags bursting at the seams, he paused and scanned the room with dark, frowning eyes. 'Where's the King Arthur book?' he said aloud. 'She'll want that. Ah . . . there it is. You're sitting on it. Off you get, cat.' He pushed me off, not giving me time to sort my paws out. I landed on the floor with a thump. I didn't want him to take the book. It was my last link to Imelda and I'd felt proud to be sitting on it, guarding it for her.

I meowed at him reproachfully.

He scowled back. 'You'll be next – cat.'

*　　*　　*

'Can you read?' Bully Boy asked me.

We were sitting side by side on a fallen log in the wild wood, our paws tucked under our bodies for warmth. He'd come to find me and I'd told him about my secret plan. I was desperate to find Imelda. I didn't trust Brad to take me to her. I needed to go, and quickly, before he put me in the travelling basket again. I remembered what he'd told Chloe: *That cat will have to go.*

But I had a clue about where to find Imelda. Brad had said she had gone somewhere she would get fit and healthy again – and only Tintagel had made her glow and her eyes shine, not so long ago. That must be where he meant. I focused on going there.

Night and day, I was wary. I wasn't going to let Brad catch me, and if he picked me up when I was asleep, I'd reverse out of his grasp. Reversing was a skill my mum cat had taught us – to be used when humans tried to trap you or give you medicine. 'They're not expecting you to reverse,' she'd said. 'That's why it works every time. When you reverse, you're much stronger. A reversing cat is unstoppable.'

I'd told Bully Boy of my plan to find my way back to Tintagel. That's when he asked me if I could read. An odd question, but he was deadly serious and I respected his intelligence.

'You know what I mean, do you?' he asked. 'Humans put squiggles on everything. They've got hundreds of different ones and they all mean something, if you can figure it out.'

'I can read a few words,' I said. 'I can read *puss* because it's on my dish. And I can read *ice cream* for when they open the freezer. And *King Arthur* 'cause it's on Imelda's book. And *tuna*, and . . .'

Bully Boy interrupted me. 'But can you read *Tintagel*?'

'Yes. I've seen it so many times. I'd recognise it.'

'What if it was on a big road sign?'

'Yes. When we went down there, Imelda kept showing it to me.'

'I've done a few journeys on my own,' Bully Boy's
eyes sparkled as he remembered, 'but always in summer.
Now is a bad time to go. The leaves are falling and the
days are getting shorter. It's hibernation time. Some
animals curl up in their burrows and they sleep until
spring. I tried it once but it didn't work for me.'

'You know so much,' I said, impressed.

'Well, I've lived a long time. Many, many years.
I'm probably old, VERY old. I feel my age in the cold
weather. My paws hurt, and my back aches when it's
cold. I expect I'll end up living in a hay barn.'

'A hay barn? What's that?'

He gave me a pitying look. 'Haven't you discovered
hay barns?'

'No.'

'Hay barns are a cat's best friend. I'll take you to
one, next time you can get away,' Bully Boy promised.
'I go there most winters. Hay barns are HOT.'

'Hot?'

'They keep you warm, like our fur does. They're
made from bales of dry grass. The farmers make them
for cows to eat in winter.'

I imagined a line of hungry cows trying to eat a barn. Surely the 'barn' would fall down, wouldn't it? I didn't want to appear stupid so I kept quiet.

'The heat and the scent of summer is stored in the hay.' Bully Boy's tone was wistful. 'You can sleep in it and be nice and warm, even in the frost. Lots of cats live in hay barns – whole families of cats and kittens, and they are mostly wild, like me. It's like a city of cats. They make tunnels and dens between the bales, and nobody ever sees them. Remember that, Merlin, because you'll be living wild on your journey. If the weather is bad and you're cold, find a hay barn. And if you don't get to Tintagel, you could live your whole life in one.'

I thought of Imelda and the dreamy nights when I'd slept on her pillow. The cuddly times, the playing and the laughter, the log fires and the hearthrug, the stack of cat food tins in the kitchen. How lonely would I be in a strange hay barn? I needed my beloved Imelda more than I cared to admit to this tough, experienced wild cat. But to be with her I had to be brave, otherwise I might never see her again and she'd be alone.

The journey was looking increasingly difficult.

'Can't you wait until spring?' Bully Boy asked.

'No. Imelda needs me.'

Bully Boy's eyes went frowny with concern. 'Humans are devious,' he warned. 'You watch out. Has he got a cage?'

'It's not really a cage. It's a travelling basket.'

'I saw a cat being caught once. They put a big wire cage in the garden where she lived, and it was a trap. They put meat in there, at one end. I told her not go in but she did, and the back door of the cage slammed shut and she was caught. I'll never, ever, forget the look in her eyes. It broke my heart. If you see a cage like that, don't go in, even if you're starving hungry.'

* * *

I actually felt sorry for Brad the following evening. He was slumped on the sofa, his eyes dull with grief. Surely I ought to give him some cat love, I reasoned, and jumped up to sit beside him. I purred and offered him a paw. He sighed and stroked me without looking at me. His touch felt wooden and insincere. 'Merlin, old son,' he said gruffly, 'you're a lovely cat. I don't dislike you. But the fact is, I can't keep you. I'll do the decent thing and take you to the RSPCA or Cats Protection, and they'll rehome you. I just want the best for you. So be a sensible cat and let me put you in the travelling basket. Don't keep running off with that fleabag Bully Boy.'

I stopped purring. Too late, I noticed he'd got the travelling basket ready at the side of the sofa. He leaned towards me and snatched me up with his strong hands, gripping me so tightly that I could hardly breathe. *Reverse,* I thought, and made my move suddenly, just when he was lowering me towards the basket. I arched my back and kicked hard with my back legs, and it worked! I sprang backwards and slipped from his grasp. Brad swore and made a lunge at me but I raced for the cat flap.

It was dark and raining. I went over the wall into Sandie's garden and crawled under her shed. A hollow place of dry, stony earth sheltered me from the weather and from Brad. I felt violated. Driven out.

Alone and sad, I crouched there, listening to the pouring rain, and the faint sound of televisions, music and laughter coming from other houses in our road. Happy houses. *Why me?* I thought. What happened to all the effort, the love and purring, and the loyalty I'd given to my human family?

I could never go back. The memory of Brad's hands lingered on my fur. I wanted to sleep but I was too upset. I sat up in my hiding place and gave myself a good wash, and debated whether to go and meow at Sandie's back door. It seemed wiser to stay hidden.

Later, I heard Brad talking to someone in the back garden. Someone I didn't know. 'Put it down here,' he said, 'and I'll ring you when the cat is in there.'

Anxious and still hurting, I tried to sleep in the cold, stony place. At least I was outside and free. Tomorrow was another day. The sun would rise and I would begin my journey to find Imelda. I thought again of Brad's words: that she'd been moved to another place where they'd help her to walk again and make her injured leg strong. *Somewhere far away,* he'd said. The only far away place I knew was Tintagel. Imelda had talked to me often about running away and even now, her backpack was under the bed crammed with stuff she'd need. I thought of the pull of home, from the north-east, when I was surrounded by the sea mist. So now, with my back almost to the rising sun, I would set off, going south-west to find Tintagel. Surely that's where she would be.

Alone but free. Alone but free. I chanted those words like a mantra as I finally went to sleep, curled up on the stones under Sandie's shed.

The rain stopped before dawn and the morning was still. Brad's car went out at the usual time. He'd gone!

I crawled out, stretched, and jumped on the wall, intending to take one last look at the home where I'd been happy and loved. I might have ventured in but something extraordinary happened.

Perched on the roof of our house was a sleek grey-and-white bird. A seagull! He saw me on the wall and took off. The rising sun burnished his wings as he glided above the garden. He sailed past me and turned his head to peer at me with a yellow eye. Round he came again, and again, each time giving me a meaningful stare. Then he returned to the roof, lifted his head to the sky and did his loud, screaming, melodic call, almost turning himself inside out with the effort.

He threw me one more look, then spread his wings and flew away to the west with his back to the sunrise. Inspired, I watched him go. I liked to think he was a messenger. A gull, from Tintagel. My seagull.

He'd come to lead me home.

I took a last peep at the garden where I'd played in the sun. I stared in disbelief. In the middle of the lawn was a rectangular wire cage and in it, at one end, was a dish of cat food. Exactly as Bully Boy had described.

It helped me make my decision. Go. Go now. And never come back.

Chapter 17

A City of Cats

I had not gone far along the streets that led to the western edge of town when I heard a thunder of paws behind me. My fur bushed out and I swung around ready to confront a dog, and there was Bully Boy, absolutely belting after me along the pavement. I'd never seen him at full gallop, and he was fast. He skidded to a halt and did three exuberant leaps like a baby lamb.

His yellow-black eyes sparkled at me. 'I'm coming with you,' he said, 'all the way.'

I was speechless. Overcome to think he would do that for me, I did purr-meows and rubbed cheeks with him.

'You're only a young cat,' he said. 'I can't let you go on your own. There are dangers you couldn't even dream about. And places you might miss – life-changing places.'

We set off, side by side at a businesslike trot. At first, I travelled proudly with my tail up, but as time passed, I began to feel ridiculous when there were no humans around to please. My tail gradually dropped and swung along behind me. Bully Boy knew exactly where to go. Once we were in the open countryside, he took me along hidden lanes and footpaths, soft for our paws and away from traffic.

Downhill, we travelled faster, twisting and turning and scampering. Enjoying ourselves. Going down and down through the woods on the side of a hill. Lower and lower, the ground getting increasingly marshy and wet. We picked our way round puddles and struggled with muddy gateways where cattle had been. I worried about my paws. They were precious. I'd always kept them immaculate and I didn't want them caked in mud. Bully Boy was much tougher than me. He barrelled onwards, under brambles and over streams, until the dappled light changed to an apple-green haze. We had reached the open fields at the end of the woods.

Bully Boy flopped down for a rest and closed his eyes, stretched out with his chin on the leafy ground. He'd seen it all before. But I sat up and gazed in astonishment at the vast, flat land before us. In the midday sun, the meadows were a luminous green and between them were bright strips of water. The level land stretched away for endless miles and the far horizon was a smudge of blue hills.

I was glad to have Bully Boy with me. On my own, I would have panicked and fled back into the woods. In my life as a young cat, I had never been so far away from houses. It was scary. Like the time when Imelda had first shown me the sky.

I wanted to go home. Lovely, predictable home where there were boundaries, and cushions, dishes of cat food and a cosy fire. I wanted Imelda. I wanted to be there for her. The blend of grief and excitement was more than I could bear. I needed to relax like Bully Boy (he was actually snoring!) but I felt too hyped to sleep. Had I made a terrible mistake? Could I really keep pace with this tough, experienced old cat?

Wash, I thought, and started cleaning the mud from my paws. Washing made my world small and manageable. By the time I'd done all four paws and my face, I was ready for a snooze.

But Bully Boy apparently had the ability to be instantly asleep, or instantly awake. He sat up and stretched. 'Let's go on,' he said. 'Wait till you see what's round the corner.'

He set off, assuming I was ready when I wasn't. I trotted after him, along the edge of the wood to the end of the hills. Around the corner was more of the level green space but there was another surprise. Lunch! In the middle of nowhere! I followed Bully Boy up a steep bank and saw a shining river, deep and mirror-like, curving gently between the high banks.

A few men sat along the bank, a long way apart. Each held a long stick over the river, from which a thin wire dangled into the water. Bundled in gloomy parkas and hats, the men were perfectly still and silent.

'What are they doing?' I asked.

'They're fishing.' Bully Boy's whiskers stuck out very straight and his nose twitched. 'Follow me,' he said, 'and you can do the meowing. Put your tail up and look thin.'

Thin? Me?

I'd never seen Bully Boy deliberately approach a human before, but he did now. He glanced round at me so I meowed. He frowned. 'Louder!' So I did the starving-kitten meow, again and again. The man swung round and saw us. His eyes twinkled between a hat and a beard and I thought he might be King Arthur.

''Ello puss. On the scrounge for a bit of fish are you? 'Ang on. I'll see what I can find.'

(Well, King Arthur wouldn't have said that.)

216

He rummaged in a yellow plastic bucket, took out two bright silver fish and threw them on the grass for us. Bully Boy gave me a triumphant stare. We were hungry. He grabbed a fish and reversed with it, growling like a dog. Then he did something beautiful and unexpected. He dropped the fish in front of me. I was moved. *He must really love me.*

He took the other one, and we carried our fish back to the edge of the wood and feasted on them. Satisfied, we rested and purred together while the November afternoon turned the fields a brassy gold, and lengthened the shadows of trees. One by one, the fishermen were packing up and trudging home along the riverbank.

Bully Boy wanted to be on the move again. He knew of a hay barn close to the river. It would be a safe place for us to sleep on the first night of our journey.

The fish had done me good but I was tired from the excitement of the day. My legs ached and a cold mist was rising from the river. I yearned for a hearthrug by a roaring fire.

'It's not far,' Bully Boy said, and I followed him along the bank of the river, past a pair of swans gliding over the water. I could hardly walk but I kept going, down a grassy track to a huddle of farm buildings. Through a dilapidated gateway was the hay barn, an enormous arched roof and no walls. A roof on legs, filled almost to the top with stacks of sweet-smelling hay. It was LUSH.

In the glow of sunset, we tiptoed inside and jumped up and up and up, the giant golden bales like steps. There were rooms and cubbyholes and dark, cat-sized doorways and tunnels, through which I glimpsed a variety of white and tabby coats and clusters of tiny kittens, their faces close together like flowers.

No one chased us. No one challenged us. The cats seemed to know Bully Boy, and accepted me because I was his sidekick. The higher we climbed, the warmer it became, and I appreciated the natural heat of the hay. It really did feel like a great storehouse of eternal summer.

A city of cats. I wished Imelda could see this.

*   *   *

My first night in a hay barn proved to be perfect for watching the stars and thinking about Imelda. She had tried to teach me about the night sky. From her bedroom window, we had studied the stars of Orion. Imelda had an app on her mobile phone which showed the star patterns in the sky, and a picture of Orion, the hunter, with the three bright stars in his belt. Then, if you looked up higher, you could see the Pleiades, which she called the Seven Sisters. From the hay barn, they were easy to see, clustered together and shining so brightly. It made me feel at home. Imelda said that even if you were far away in a distant land, the stars were the same.

I wondered if she was looking at Orion and the Pleiades too, and thinking of me. She'd told me about the music of the spheres, a secret music from the distant stars. We'd listened together in her bedroom window and I heard it, just as I'd heard the dolphins. It was music only cats could hear. We cats know and hear and sense far more than humans. We don't put our sacred knowledge into words. We use it.

I used it now as I listened from the hay barn. It made my fur bush out and my whiskers come alive like antennae, receiving encoded music from the mysterious universe. I was better than a mobile phone. I could see Imelda. I could talk to her.

Our spiritual bond was strong, but I was OK, and she wasn't. She'd lost her mum and her home. To me, the memory of Brad's mood as he gathered Imelda's stuff into bags was intensely upsetting. Especially when he'd pushed me off the King Arthur book. No one on earth could understand how a ginger cat had become so emotionally attached – to a book! Only my angel knew, and she came to me swiftly, making herself almost invisible, not attracting the attention of any of the life in and around the barn.

I felt like a very small cat made of golden silk, like the one on the embroidered cushion. A little gem of a cat who shone like a jewel within the great heart of an angel. I'd been wounded by all that had happened in my young life. The fireworks. The policeman holding Imelda's helmet. The shock of seeing Imelda in hospital, her beautiful eyes blank and unresponsive. Brad trying to force me into the cat cage. The night on the cold stones under Sandie's shed. The courage I'd needed to make my decision to go on this journey.

It was a lot for a sensitive young cat who only wanted to bring love and happiness to the world.

One by one, my angel healed those festering wounds by sending them into the sacred flame of unconditional love. Each wound dissolved into the light, like sugar crystals in water. And each time, I felt myself becoming warm, and soft, and whole. An exuberant, strong and loving ginger cat. Who I was born to be.

I was ecstatic. *Hello, Merlin. You're BACK*. I wanted a mad half hour in the hay barn – but that had to wait.

'Let us visit Imelda,' my angel said, 'and we will help her, not with words but with love and beautiful colours and . . .'

'And purring,' I added.

'And purring, indeed. Purring is wordless prayer. Begin it now.' My angel went quiet and together we visualised Imelda. We sent her love, and peace, and hope. Especially hope. We showed her a golden door she could open and we gave her courage to change, and allow herself to accept the treatment she was being given.

I sent Imelda a personal message: I loved her. And one day, we'd meet again – in Tintagel. And, at last, I saw a flicker of hope in her eyes, a shift in the numbness, a way out of the despair. Now, I just had to make it to Tintagel.

'It will take time,' my angel said, 'but she will get well. Every night, Merlin, send her the healing light again.'

'I will.'

The time of healing under the stars with my angel came to an end, and for a moment I sat remembering how it felt to be a shining cat. I settled down again next to Bully Boy, and in his sleep he reached out a long black paw and put it over my back. It felt good.

* * *

In the morning, I was awake first. I disentangled myself from Bully Boy and sat watching him. His features were vulnerable and serene when he was asleep, his mouth curved in a sort of smile. For the first time, I noticed he wasn't completely black. On his forehead was a small, heart-shaped pip of white fur, and his left front paw had a white 'sock'. There were a few grey hairs around his muzzle and along the bridge of his nose. He was old and nobody cared for him. Would he last the journey? And what would he do in Tintagel? *Imelda will care for him,* I thought.

The morning sky glowered with clouds. I made my way to the edge of the hay bales and gazed down into the barn. At one end, the bales were stacked at lower and lower levels until there was a patch of floor, covered in wisps of hay. Cats were everywhere, high and low, sitting on the bales. The way they were all facing in one direction told me something was about to happen.

Beyond the barn was the back yard of a farmhouse. The door opened and a white-haired woman in brightly coloured clothes appeared carrying a tray twice as wide as her dumpy body. Ooh, I could smell what was on it. Dish upon dish of cat food. The woman gave a shrill call which echoed into the barn roof.

'Cat. Cat. Cat. CAT.' She carried the tray towards the barn. 'Cat. Cat. Cat. CAT.'

A chorus of meows greeted her and the barn cats leapt down from the bales and converged on her in a forest of tails. Instantly awake, Bully Boy sailed over-head and bounded down there. Did 'Cat. Cat. Cat. CAT,' mean me? Why not? I descended gracefully, and added my fluffy ginger tail to the forest.

The woman had put the dishes on the barn floor and the cats were eating daintily, not growling but sharing nicely. I was impressed. They seemed to know there was plenty. Even the young kittens had time to come wobbling and tumbling down the bales to get their share.

The woman returned to the farmhouse and emerged again with a second lot of dishes, this time filled with creamy milk and mounds of dried Go-Cat. I'd never shared a dish with another cat before but it was quite pleasant to feel a sleek body and a set of whiskers on each side of me.

When I'd had enough, I noticed the woman sitting on a hay bale, obviously enjoying watching the com-munity of cats and kittens. I ran to her and jumped up beside her. 'Well,' she remarked, surprised and pleased, 'you're a lovely cat. Where did you come from?' She let me sit on her lap and purr, and I did my best to give her some love and say thank you. 'You're not a feral cat, are you? I wonder if you're lost. I'll bet someone is crying over you.' She examined my collar. 'Ah, you are someone's pet cat. Merlin.'

It was good to hear my name. I leaned against the vivid colours of her sweater and let her fiddle with my collar. 'What a shame,' she said. 'Your name is there but the medallion's gone so we don't know where you live.' I remembered leaving it caught on a twig in the woods. 'Shall I take you inside by the fire? I think I should ring Cats Protection about you. I wonder if you've got a microchip.'

She picked me up and I was going to go with her when I heard the cry of a seagull. He took off from the roof of the farmhouse and glided around the outside of the barn, again turning his head to look at me with one yellow eye. Clearly he was warning me. Spooked, I reversed out of the woman's arms and fled back to the top of the haystack where Bully Boy was washing.

I was too trusting. How easy I made it for people to catch me and shut me in! Without Bully Boy, I'd soon regress to being a carpet cat and then I'd never see Imelda again.

The rain fell heavily all that day, hammering on the barn roof so loudly that other sounds were drowned. We opted to stay put and spent a second night in the barn – another good, safe, warm sleep followed by a communal breakfast. It suited me. I'd have happily stayed and made friends with the other cats, if it weren't for my mission to find Imelda.

Well fed and rested, we set off again the next morning, following the riverbank across the levels, watching the extraordinary flocks of starlings making their shifting, swerving patterns in the sky. Imelda had once told me how the birds flew thousands of miles to spend the summer in a distant country, and nobody knew how they managed to do it. How did they find their way?

Despite the peace of the levels, something was wrong. A sound of something powerful, a continuous roar, and we were going towards it. Soon I could feel it in my paws. The land hummed and quivered, the gates and the stiles rang with it. Why was Bully Boy heading towards it with such confidence, his head down?

I followed him, nervously, wanting to stop, wanting to turn around and flee from this unknown, intrusive force. It had a smell which tainted the air across the green fields. We were breathing its poison.

It might kill me. I suddenly felt muzzy-headed and ill. I could hardly breathe. The bad air hung over the tips of the grasses, right at our noses. There was no escaping it.

I panicked, turned around and ran for the hills.

Chapter 18

The Day of the Snow

Bully Boy hurtled after me. I was shocked when he gave me a swipe. His power made me fall over and become a defenceless kitten. I hissed at him, and he glared down with black eyes. 'What do you think you're doing?' he asked furiously.

'The air is bad,' I gasped. 'It's killing us.'

'No, it's not – but it could kill us if we hang around. We've got to keep going. We HAVE to cross the big road,' Bully Boy insisted. 'The way to the sea is the other side of it. I'm going fast because I've done this before. There's only one way for cats to cross it, and it's a bridge. I know where it is. So follow me, and don't mess about.'

'I can't. It's killing me.'

'Yes, you CAN. Think of Tintagel and follow me. When we get to the other side, there's a hill with pine trees.'

'I feel sick.'

'Me too. We'll get through it, Merlin. Don't give up. Just tell your paws to keep running. I'm with you and I won't let you die.'

I looked into his frowny eyes and saw a glow of courage there. Bully Boy was an old, old cat. Why was he doing this for me?

Inspired by his strength, I dragged myself up and shook my ginger fur. I told my paws to keep running, and I held the vision he had given me. A hill with pine trees. A hill with pine trees. A hill . . .

I studied the backs of his paws as the big cat ran ahead of me. Scruffy and strong. His tail thin. His bitten-down ears flicking back to check if I was following. Bully Boy was a true friend. Ashamed of my panic, I kept going.

The sky was a brilliant blue, and a white bird was circling high up, tiny, but perfect. Not flapping his wings but gliding on the wind. My seagull! I was never sure if he was really watching me, or if he simply happened to be there.

We drew close to the dreadful road. I saw the haze of pollution and the deathly speed of cumbersome lorries. I heard their rhythmic rumble and the whine of fast cars. The seagull was sailing high in the blue, crossing the impossible road with ease and grace.

Then I spotted the bridge, arched like a rainbow, and it gave me hope.

Bully Boy led me up a track alongside the road and on to the narrow bridge. He looked round at me and lashed his tail. 'Here we go!' The yellow was back in his eyes in a wicked sparkle. 'Let's do it in style.' He flexed his back, kinked his tail and took off like a kitten, stampeding up and over the bridge.

OK, I thought. Fired with rebellious joy, I sped after him. We flew. Two wild cats madly crossing the terrible road, galloping over a bridge in the sky, sailing like the seagull.

On the other side, the air was fresh, blowing all the way from the sea. Still Bully Boy wouldn't stop. On and on we ran, across vast stubble fields and meadows full of sheep. In the light of the noontime sun, we trotted up the promised hill to the summit where the west wind sang through the pine trees. My headache vanished and the air sparkled in my lungs, tasting of pine and sea salt.

I knew immediately why Bully Boy had brought us here. This hilltop was a power point on the earth's secret magnetic grid. While Bully Boy collapsed for his midday sleep, I stayed awake to sit and gaze and feel the buzz of those invisible golden pathways. I didn't have to think, I just allowed my soul to open up like a flower and let the knowledge flow.

Tintagel. Where exactly was it? I remembered the cottage where we had stayed and the rock shaped like a chair where I'd sat with Josephine. It was easy to do. I found myself turning to face the direction of our route. All I needed to know was there for me, in the ancient leys of the earth. The way to Tintagel glinted like a skein of gossamer. It showed me landmarks. Church towers, Celtic crosses, holy wells and hills with pine trees, like this one. I wouldn't always be able to see them but it didn't matter. My psi sense would keep us on track and, if there were obstacles, we'd go round them. I had no idea at the time exactly how vast some of those obstacles would be.

When Bully Boy woke up, he wanted to talk. To my surprise, he apologised for swiping me. Of course I forgave him and we were still the best of friends. I asked him why he wanted to help with the journey.

He looked thoughtful. 'You're the best cat in my life,' he said, 'and helping you is the only good thing I've ever done. I'm a wicked old cat, and I've had to be. You're a good cat – a shining cat – and you're like a light in my life. You and Imelda are the only ones who have loved me.'

I hardly knew what to say, so I purred and rubbed my head against his. I was proud to be his friend.

Then he said something shocking and disturbing.

'I'm going to die soon. I wanted to put my life right.'

'But you're not ill,' I said, alarmed.

'No, I'm just OLD,' Bully Boy sighed, 'and I'd like to spend my old age with you and Imelda. I might come inside sometimes when it's freezing cold, and warm my aching back by the fire. It's something I've never done.'

I was moved. We sat close, side by side. 'Imelda would never hurt you,' I said, 'and she wouldn't shut you in either.'

'I couldn't get through one of those cat flaps,' Bully Boy said. 'I'm too big. I tried once and got stuck. It gave me a fright.'

'Imelda would make a bigger one for you. Imelda's clever. She wants to be a vet.'

'A vet? What's that?'

'A person who makes animals better when they're sick. Haven't you ever been to one?'

'No.'

There was nothing more to say. Bully Boy's life had been so different from mine.

He'd never lived with a human. But he had told me he liked Imelda, and how she was the only human who had shown him kindness and respect. As we trotted on, side by side, I tried to explain how I'd helped Imelda by purring, and by listening, and by sometimes making her laugh. 'Over time, we've grown really close,' I said. 'She needs me. I can help her to feel good about herself.'

While we were talking, the sun was slowly lengthening the shadows of trees and buildings, making the long gold bars of afternoon light. Some of them stretched for miles across the fields.

'We should find a hay barn,' I said.

'Oh, there is one. I know it well,' Bully Boy said, 'and, if we're quick, we'll get some food before night.'

I followed him, satisfied with our day. Surely the worst was over. What could be worse than crossing the big road? But how long was it going to take us to reach Tintagel? The days were getting colder and shorter. There were still red berries in the hedges for the birds. What would happen when it was winter? I didn't know and couldn't imagine.

*   *   *

On the day of the snow, we had been on our journey for weeks. It seemed endless. We hadn't seen the sea but it was close enough for the air to taste of salt and for the trees to be bent over, away from the westerly winds.

We were both tired but we hadn't gone hungry. I learned fast, from watching Bully Boy, how to find and catch mice, how to fish in some of the pools and streams. Sometimes Bully Boy would crouch on a rock and snatch a trout big enough for us to share. When we passed through villages, it was my turn to be the provider. I became a brazen thief, going into strange houses through the cat flaps and coming out with whatever I could grab from a table or a cat dish. Pieces of roast chicken, wedges of cheese, slices of ham. Nothing was safe from me, and I was swift and stealthy. I never got caught.

But I hated it. I hated being the baddie. I hated upsetting humans I might have made friends with. And on cold, wet days, I'd catch a glimpse of a blazing fire or feel the warmth from a stove. Mostly I hated it when someone yelled at me.

I felt BAD. My tail had forgotten how to go up and look friendly. My cherished ability to purr and to heal and love people was no longer needed. My fur lost its gloss and I was sure that my eyes had lost their sparkle. I didn't like myself at all. I was a nameless nobody.

I told myself it wasn't for ever. We'd get to Tintagel, find Imelda, and my life as a healing cat would be restored. Bully Boy was my only friend in the world. We kept each other warm and shared our food.

How I missed my playtimes and the nights on Imelda's pillow, and the interactions I'd had with my humans.

When the first snowflakes came, we were high up on heather-covered moorland and I had just touched noses with a pony, a mother with a baby foal. The weather was bitterly cold and the pony seemed to be actually generating heat with her thick fuzzy coat. She touched noses with me very gently, not blowing too much hot breath at me.

Bully Boy was having his midday sleep under a gnarled old hawthorn tree. I'd never seen snow before and had no idea what it was and what it might do. To me, it was pure magic. Big white flakes fluttering down (from the sky!) and vanishing when they landed. At first, there were only a few and I loved playing with them. I hadn't played for so long. I leapt and chased, trying to catch one between my paws, but when I did, it disappeared. I jumped higher and higher and did some spectacular pounces but never caught a single snowflake. Only the laughter was missing. The ponies watched me with peaceful brown eyes, and when the snow came thick and fast they lay down in a communal clump and tucked their legs under, keeping each other warm.

I was warm from my exercise but Bully Boy wasn't. His coat was cold and he woke up shivering. I pressed myself close to heat him up. He wasn't pleased to see the snow. To him, it was a catastrophe.

'I didn't think it would snow so soon. We must get down off these hills,' he said. 'Snow is bad for a wild cat.'

'Why? What does it do?'

'It makes you wet, like rain, only worse,' he said. 'Look at you – you're wet already.'

I shook my fur and drops flew out and I realised my paws were soaking.

'It's wet now,' Bully Boy said, 'but in the night the snow turns into ice. We don't want ice in our fur.'

It was early afternoon but the clouds were heavy and grey like a wood pigeon. The snow fell thicker and thicker. I was mesmerised and fascinated by the whirling flakes that pitched on to the ground, covering it in a crust of white. When I ventured out in it, my paws made little holes. I longed to play again. If only I had a cat friend like Josephine who would enjoy this marvellous snow.

Bully Boy seemed afraid and that wasn't like him. How could a tough wild cat be nervous of these drifting snowflakes? I didn't understand, but he looked so miserable that I cuddled up to him again. 'We won't be able to move on in the snow,' he said. 'We must shelter where we can. It might be many days before we can go on.'

I was disappointed. We were so close to Tintagel, I was sure of it. I put those feelings aside and tried to be kind and loyal to Bully Boy. He'd left his life and his home to help me on our journey and he'd been determined to get us there. He wasn't going to give up. I loved him and if he wanted to sit in the snow, then I'd sit in the snow with him.

Together we investigated a dense thicket of gorse and low-growing trees, all leaning away from the sea. It was warmer under there and the ground was dry. We settled down in a hollow of soft earth with a canopy of branches overhead. It was almost cosy. I was OK, but Bully Boy still shivered. He didn't want to talk but closed his eyes. We'd had nothing to eat. I was torn between staying with him to keep him warm or trying to catch mice. 'Don't leave me, Merlin,' he pleaded. So I stayed and gave him everything I could. Purring. Kneading with my paws. Licking him dry. Warming and loving him. Remembering how, once, he'd done the same for me when I fell in the pond.

The night seemed to go on for ever. I heard the soft patter of the falling snow and the comforting sound of the ponies breathing and shuffling around.

In the morning, an ice-cold, crystalline light filtered through our canopy. I crept out into a white and silent world, muffled by a crust of glistening snow. I soon found myself playing and skidding until Bully Boy appeared. He still didn't like the snow but he looked better.

We were marooned for two nights in our shelter under the bushes. We lived on mice and a rabbit which Bully Boy caught. Then the wind swung round to the west and the air grew warm. The snow began to thaw and we were on the move again.

Tintagel was easy to recognise. It had a ruined castle on a rocky island and a big, square hotel on the cliffs. We had a moment of euphoria when we came over the brow of the last hill and there, before us, was a dark blue sea with white-capped waves. And I suddenly saw the big square hotel in the distance.

'That's IT,' I said. 'Tintagel.'

I wanted to laugh and cry, like a human. I wanted to dance and sing. The long journey was over.

'Tintagel? Is that it? Are we here?'

If cats could smile, then Bully Boy was doing it right now. His eyes glowed yellow and sparkled. 'We've DONE it,' he said. 'We've DONE it.'

For a moment, we stood on the hillside, fizzing with excitement.

And for the first time ever, Bully Boy played with me. He did three great leaps, like a baby lamb. We chased each other. We skidded on the ice. We leapt in the air with our paws open like flowers. And there just happened to be a seagull who swooped past us, turned his head and looked at us with a yellow eye, and flew on, doing his melodic cry, soaring down and down into Tintagel.

Then we sat close and gazed at the sea, dreaming and planning the life we would live in Tintagel – with Imelda.

'I've never been happy like this before,' Bully Boy said. 'I've always been so focused on survival I forgot what it's like to play.'

'I'd play, no matter what,' I said. 'It does me good – and it makes humans laugh. Playing makes the world a better place.'

'Let's move on.' Bully Boy got up and stretched. 'I want to see your cave – Merlin's Cave.'

'We'll go down there,' I said, surprised. On one of our hay barn nights, I'd tried to tell him Imelda's favourite legend about the ship of light and the nine great waves, and how the ninth wave had brought a baby boy who grew up to be a king. Bully Boy had listened with a sceptical frown.

* * *

Our journey ended at sunset, the sea ablaze with the sun's reflection. We were tired and hungry with no energy left to search for a meal when we had a lucky encounter on the coastal path. A man plodded towards us laden down with fisherman's gear, probably on his way home. Our noses twitched. We looked at each other with one thought. Fish! Bully Boy retreated to a safe rock while I stood in the man's way, doing my starving-kitten meow. His blue eyes glinted from under his cap. 'I know what you'm wantin',' he chuckled and took an extraordinary fish out of his bucket. 'Here ya are.' He threw it on the grass and I was pleased to see it was big enough for both me and Bully Boy. He walked on, laughing, and we dragged the fish behind a rock and feasted on it.

'This has been the best day of my whole life,' Bully Boy said. 'The fun we had playing. The easy path. The sunset. The fish.'

I was happy for him. I started purring and he joined in. Together we purred and rested, tucked into the soft clumps of thrift at the foot of a rock, sheltered and secluded. We'd had a perfect day but something wasn't right. I noticed that Bully Boy was breathing too fast. I asked him what was wrong. His eyes were black and dilated. 'It happens sometimes,' he admitted, 'when I'm tired. It's just old age . . . and . . .'

'And what?' I asked when he hesitated.

'I get a pain in my chest. It goes away if I rest.'

Concerned, I pressed myself close to him. I remembered how he had shivered in the snow. Had it made him ill? If it had, there would only be me to help him recover. Should I have let him play so wildly? It hadn't seemed wrong when he'd been happy.

'Merlin,' he said, 'remember this. You changed my life. You showed me good things and you gave me hope.'

'I'm glad. But you concentrate on breathing and get some sleep. Then you'll feel better.' I watched him close his eyes and I purred him to sleep. He looked peaceful.

I wanted to go into the village of Tintagel and find the holiday cottage where I'd stayed with Sandie and Imelda. I hoped Josephine might be there in the garden. But Bully Boy wanted to sleep and he didn't like going into places where there were houses and people. 'OK,' I said, 'I'll just go and sit on top of the rock and have a look around. I won't leave you.'

Then he said something strange. 'I'm going to have a lovely sleep, Merlin. Keep watch with me.'

Puzzled, I gave him a kiss and went to sit above him on top of the high rock. It was a clear, starry night and I could see the village, bright lights shining from the windows of the houses.

The voice of my angel came to me unexpectedly. 'Go back to your friend. The big black cat. He needs you, Merlin. Beautiful Boy is coming home.'

Chapter 19

A Random Act of Kindness

Beautiful Boy? It took me a minute to understand what the angel meant. She'd changed his name! Why hadn't I done that for him? And what did she mean about him 'coming home'?

I jumped down from the rock and ran to Bully Boy. He had moved right back into a crack in the rock and I squeezed in there with him. His breathing was worse. Not fast, but spaced out. I remembered Chloe and suddenly I knew what was happening. I didn't believe it because I couldn't bear it.

My love would keep him alive. I'd purr and keep him warm and encourage him. I put my paws around his neck and did little purr-meows. *Don't go. Don't leave me,* I thought, and my own heart raced with anxiety. I prayed to the angels, 'Don't take him. Don't take my best friend. Can't he stay?'

Bully Boy sensed my desperation. He half-opened his old eyes and looked at me as if from a distance. He wanted to say something. I waited, in denial, not accepting that this was my last chance to gaze into his beloved face.

At last he spoke. 'It's time for me to go. I'll be back, some day, and I'll live with you and Imelda. We'll take care of her together.'

I tried to speak but he lifted his paw and touched my cheek with it, so gently, and he said, 'Be quiet and let me go, Merlin – till we meet again.'

Then he took one more breath. His body heaved with it and let go with a deep sigh, his paws curled, his face endearingly peaceful.

It was beautiful, and it was terrible.

The two words burned in my soul like twin flames.

How would I live without Bully Boy? I had nothing, and nobody, and no home. No fire. No place to sleep. But I still believed I must help Imelda. She was my priority, and Bully Boy loved her too. He'd brought me to Tintagel to find her, and it had cost him his life.

I couldn't leave him. Numb with desolation and shock, I stayed close, my paws still hugging him. Bully Boy had helped me on my journey. Now, surely, my love would help him on his journey into the shining lands.

Eventually I slept, lulled by the sound of the waves and distant music from the village. My dreams were vivid and enlightening. 'Beautiful Boy' had been transformed on that day in the wild wood when he'd climbed to the top of the beech tree, and I'd looked back and seen him as a tiny new cat in the heart of an angel. Beautiful Boy had turned out to be my best friend. I hung on to the words he'd spoken. 'Till we meet again. I'll be back, some day . . .'

I woke just before dawn and found his dear old body cold. I didn't want to touch it any more but I couldn't leave it. I sat up, suddenly alert and listening to the singing coming from the sea.

Dolphins!

It was too dark to see them but I heard their song and understood. The dolphins knew there had been a death; the soul of a very special black cat was sitting at the foot of the rainbow bridge. The dolphins sang for him and Beautiful Boy began to move, tentatively at first, up the high curve of the bridge, then eagerly running with his tail up. His coat became glossy and he looked young again. The dolphins sang him over the bridge, with other cats and dogs, beginning so nervously, then gaining confidence and finally scampering down the other side.

For him, it was joyful. Or was it? Bully Boy had loved being on earth. He'd told me that many times.

For me, it was rock bottom. In a dark bubble of despair, I lay there not knowing or caring what I would do next. I couldn't move his body or cover it, and to walk away and leave it there was unthinkable.

Had it not been for the kindness of a stranger, I might have given up and stayed there.

''Ello puss. All right, are you?'

From inside my bubble of despair I saw a homely pair of boots appear before me, and felt a sense of warmth close to me. It was the man who had given us the fish. My eyes must have been dull and expressionless for the boots left the path and came clumping over the grass to me. 'What's the matter, old fella?' He spotted Bully Boy's lifeless body. 'Oh dear, oh dear, poor old cat. What happened, eh?'

All I could manage was a silent meow.

'Your mate, was he?'

Another silent meow.

'Can I pick you up?'

I wasn't sure but I let him and once I was close to the glint of kindness in his blue eyes, I felt rescued. His heart was beating steadily and he was holding me close to it. I was too numb to purr.

He put me down. 'You sit there,' he said, ''cause I'm gonna give your mate a decent funeral.' I sat like a wooden cat, half-grieving, half-watching.

The man knelt down on the wet grass and took a knife from his haversack. He cut a strip of turf and put it on one side. Then he picked up a piece of slate and used it like a shovel, digging a shallow grave. He whistled a tune while he worked and it had a calming effect on me. I wasn't sure what he was trying to do.

'You might not like this,' he warned, 'but it's gotta be done.' Still whistling the lovely tune, he picked a few of the yellow and white flowers that were still in bloom. 'Good job this is Cornwall,' he added. 'There's always a flower, even in the colder months.' He put the posy down in front of me. 'You look after those and I'll do the business – what's gotta be done.'

I winced as he picked up Bully Boy's body and gently lowered it into the hole. 'Now, you come and say goodbye,' he said, 'like this.' He stroked Bully Boy's fur and whispered to him, 'Sleep sweetly, old fella. You're at peace.'

I made myself go and look, one last time, at my beloved friend, but I didn't want to touch him. Bully Boy wasn't there any more. He was free. He'd crossed the rainbow bridge.

The man covered him up tenderly and with respect, levelling the soil with his hands. He replaced the strip of turf and carefully pressed the edges down. Then he gathered some pebbles and arranged them in a cross on top of the grave and laid the flowers, slowly and with great love. He whispered some words and we both stared at the grave.

To my surprise, the man picked me up again and stroked me. His blue eyes glinted into my soul. 'Your friend would want you to be happy and get on with your life, wouldn't he?'

I managed a very silent meow.

'That's what you've gotta do. Don't hang around here and be miserable. You're a lovely cat. You go home and get on with your life. And if I come by and see you here again, we'll have a cuddle. OK?'

He put me down on the rock. 'Bye, now.' I watched him walk on his way, warmed in body and soul. His kindness stayed with me like a soft blanket and the tune he'd been whistling danced in my heart.

I felt better.

I'd try to get on with my life. *Find Imelda,* I thought, and decided to go to the holiday cottage where we had stayed. If she wasn't there, I'd search the village for her.

I stretched and shook my fur. It wasn't glossy but matted and dull after the long weeks of living wild. Imelda used to enjoy brushing me.

Before setting off, I spotted the seagull on the rock stack, sitting like a duck with his feet tucked under himself as if he meant to stay put.

He gave me a sort of nod. Was he telling me he would watch over Bully Boy's grave?

*   *   *

The cottage garden was overgrown compared to the neat square of lawn it had been when we'd stayed there. I inspected the cottage. The door and windows were shut and no smoke came from the chimney. It looked cold and empty. Cautiously, I jumped on to a windowsill and peeped in. Imelda would have had a fire burning and a lamp glowing. Her books and shoes would be lying around and the TV or music would be on.

I went round to the back and pressed my nose against the kitchen window. It was bare and shiny. I remembered the dishes of tuna and chicken she'd given me on the floor. What an easy, pampered life I'd had. I felt years older. Wiser. Tough, like Bully Boy. And scruffy. And broken-hearted.

Obviously, Imelda wasn't there. I resolved to check the place each day in case she turned up. OK, I might be scruffy and thin, but I still had lots of love to give. Dreams of how happy our first meeting would be sustained me. How would I tell her about Bully Boy? It was impossible.

The angel had told me to send love and healing to Imelda, and I'd tried, despite being cold and hungry. Imelda must be missing me. What would she be doing at this moment? The last time I'd seen her was the day Sandie took me to the hospital. Was her broken leg better? Could she walk again? Brad had said she was going to a rehabilitation unit, and I was still sure that meant Tintagel – it must be somewhere other than the cottage, that was all. Imelda had told me so many times that Tintagel was where she wanted to go. I tingled with excitement at the thought of finding her. What would Imelda do if she knew how sad and lost I was? She'd cry if she saw me now. She'd give me love and attention, and let me sleep on her pillow.

I decided to spend the night in the garden, curled up in a sheltered corner, and watch to see if anyone came to the cottage. The front door had an open porch with a shelf inside. I trotted round to inspect it and discovered there was a cushion on it! Perfect! I tried it and fell asleep instantly.

'Look at him now,' said the angel in my dream. A shining cat came towards me, and it was Bully Boy. His eyes were pure gold and sparkling with wisdom and love. The frown had gone. His jet-black fur shone like lustrous velvet. His tail was up, tall and straight. His ears were perfect. We touched noses and I felt very small and earthbound, and honoured to have this shining cat as a friend.

The dream inspired me, and I'd found a place to sleep. Two positives. I slept for hours, but woke up cold and very hungry.

Wary of the traffic and the people walking about, I ran down the road and came to a shop that smelled deliciously of ham and cheese. I went in with my tail up and quickly got evicted. 'No cats in here.' A girl in a smart overall shooed me out, but I wouldn't go. I sat on the floor of the shop and did the starving-kitten meow. 'You poor cat.' The girl picked me up and carried me outside, and shut the door. I sat meowing and people noticed me. I shot in again when someone opened the door.

'He must be a stray.'

'He's very persistent. He must be hungry.'

'Poor thing. He's a lovely cat.'

'But we can't have him in here. Hygiene and all that.'

I wasn't going to give up. Every time they evicted me, I waited my chance and shot in again. I actually found the display of cat food (tins with happy cats on them) and sat looking up at it and meowing piteously.

'You cheeky cat,' the portly shop manager said. 'If I give you something, will you go away?'

'Yes,' I meowed, and wove myself around her ankles with my tail waving. She sighed. 'Give him one of those little tubs, Bel – outside.'

The girl, Bel, asked me what I would like! 'Gourmet Tuna? Or Whiskas Rabbit?' I meowed for Whiskas Rabbit. I couldn't believe how easy it had been. I didn't have to steal. The kindness in her voice gave me another boost. Nothing had ever tasted so delicious as the contents of that little tinfoil dish. I scoffed every last morsel and chased the dish down the pavement.

Darkness came early but Tintagel had street lights and the glow from cottage windows. In the cold air, I sat up on a wall, washing diligently. I was still too numb and upset to play.

Finding Imelda was priority and I closely watched all the people who were plodding along the street, going in and out of the brightly lit shops. Imelda would see me on the wall and hold out her arms. She'd laugh and cry and hold me close, and wrap a warm scarf around my cold, aching body. And I would make her happy again.

I stayed on the wall for a long time, politely acknowl-
edging people who noticed me, and children who stood
on tiptoe to stroke me. Being unresponsive didn't come
naturally to me. I was waiting for Imelda, but there was
no sign of her.

One by one, the bright shops closed and people went
home. In the deserted street, a few hailstones scattered
down from the bitterly cold sky. Some people walked
by with a dog on a lead, and the dog had a coat on.
I'd never needed a silly coat with my thick ginger ruff
of fur, but now a wave of jealousy washed over me.
Why me? Why was I nobody's cat? Where were the
cats who lived in Tintagel? Inside, rolling on rugs in
front of fires.

Suddenly, my heart leapt with excitement. Imelda
and Sandie were walking briskly on the other side of
the street. Surely that was Sandie, marching along in
her heavy coat and boots – and Imelda, with her hair
in a bouncy pompom, swanning along with the pink-
and-grey backpack?

My calling meow echoed from the walls. I jumped
down, crossed the road between cars, and went
belting after the pair on cold paws. Meowing and
meowing. But they didn't turn round. With my pulse
racing, I sped after them down a side street, seeing

their silhouettes under the street lamps. I couldn't wait for the moment when Imelda would turn and see me, and cry, 'MERLIN', and scoop me into her arms. I'd kiss her face and purr as she carried me home, and we'd be together for ever.

Still they didn't turn, so I overtook them at full gallop and sat on the pavement in front of them, my fur fluffed out, my eyes full of hope and love.

'Oh, look at that cat,' the girl said, and she squatted down to stroke me.

My whole world collapsed. It wasn't Imelda. It wasn't Sandie.

I'd got it wrong. So wrong.

'I don't like cats,' said the woman who looked like Sandie, and they both marched on down the street.

Bitterly disappointed, I turned and crept away, low to the ground, hardly noticing where I was going. Drunk with grief, I wandered back to the main street and found a dark corner where I pressed myself against the cold, cold wall. I shut my eyes and dozed, not wanting to move. What if Imelda hadn't come to Tintagel?

I should head back to the cottage, and the cushion in the porch, but I couldn't be bothered.

About an hour later, when I was even colder, things started to happen in the street. Purposeful footsteps plodded past me. People were gathering by the pub. They were putting on fluorescent orange gilets over their coats, and carrying red collecting tins on loops of cord. 'Good luck, guys. Hope you raise lots of money. Meet back here later, OK?'

'See you later!'

'See you later!'

The cheerful voices woke me up. It felt like an opportunity for me, but I wasn't sure what it might bring. Then I heard the voice of my angel, 'Follow them, Merlin.'

The thump of drums and the sound of music came out of the pub. It seemed to give energy and courage to the group of fundraisers.

Not knowing why, I trotted after them hopefully, and that was how I found Theo.

Chapter 20

Theo

On my first morning with Theo, I woke up and thought I was in heaven. Toasty warm, well fed, blissfully comfortable on a sumptuous pillow next to Theo. I lay there luxuriating, gently rolling and stretching. Life and light was in my eyes again. I could feel it.

From outside came the glorious sounds of dawn on the North Cornish coast. The voice of the sea, sighing and burbling. The whirling chorus of seagulls, high up, circling over the village and the cliffs. Was my seagull up there with them? Or was he stoically parked on the rock above Bully Boy's grave? Would the man who had buried my friend walk by and pause to send a prayer to the dear old cat who had brought me here, a hundred miles across country, to Tintagel?

Theo was still asleep. I studied his sleeping face. The deep wrinkles on his brow and at the corners of his eyes.

The florid, weather-beaten cheeks. The silver-white of his beard. He looked clean and dignified, and he was a quiet sleeper, his hands folded, his nails immaculate.

My new friend. Theo. Intense gratitude filled my heart. The love between a human and a cat is something to be treasured and nurtured. I made up my mind to take good care of Theo. I didn't yet know what he needed but I'd watch and listen. Together, we would heal the wounds of the past and find our way back to trust and contentment.

Theo's bedroom was upstairs and he slept with the top window open and the curtains drawn back. In the night, I peeped at the stars without lifting my head from the pillow. I wanted to explore my new home but Theo needed me to be there when he opened his eyes. It would be an unforgettable moment.

My grief for Bully Boy would come and go but having a secure and loving home made a difference. The longing for Imelda would always be in my heart, and I'd continue to send her love and healing. Perhaps someday we would find each other. I wasn't ready to give up, but I also didn't know where to search for her. I'd been so sure that she'd be in Tintagel.

Theo was stirring, so I put my chin on the pillow ready for him to look into my eyes and realise his loneliness was over. He had a loyal friend: me.

He reached out and touched my fur. It made him smile. He opened his eyes and we gazed at each other. I did my best purr-meow, and he nearly cried. 'Aw, you beautiful friend,' he murmured. 'You're like sunshine to an old man's soul.'

I stared into the glistening blue of his eyes and patted him with my paw. I knew he couldn't speak because he wanted to cry, so I purred, and the quiet rhythm rolled out a sense of peace. Theo sighed. He went back to sleep for a few minutes and when he woke again, I was still there, purring (business as usual!).

This time, his eyes were open wide and he swung himself out of bed, picked me up and stood in the window, surveying the sea and sky. A seagull (was it HIM?) was perched on the gatepost. 'That's Archie,' Theo said. 'He'll be wanting his breakfast, like you.'

'If I'd known you were coming, I'd have got you a cat bed,' he said as he carried me downstairs, 'but there's plenty of cat food – and later on, you can have some of my roast chicken. Now, what would you like, eh? How about this one?' He held up a sachet with a tabby cat on the front. 'Whiskas Tuna.'

While he opened it, I wove myself around his legs. He gave me two dishes – milk and the tuna. While I was eating it, he went outside and threw some stuff down for the seagull. 'Good morning, Archie!'

In the kitchen was a stove called an Aga and even the floor in front of it was warm. I sat close to it and washed and stared in astonishment at what Theo was doing. He wasn't eating breakfast. He was doing press-ups on the floor. Then he messed about with two heavy dumbbells, lifting them up and down, and getting hot and breathless. Was he having a mad half hour? Should I join in?

I remembered how Bully Boy had enjoyed playing in the snow. At least he had died happy. And I'd been there for him.

While Theo was in the shower, I popped out through the cat flap. Archie had flown away. In the distance, on the rocky hillside, I spotted the lone seagull parked on top of a rock. 'Archie' was obviously a highly intelligent, interesting bird. Perhaps he knew where to find Imelda.

Inside, Theo was cooking and singing. I discovered how much I liked music. The power of his voice went right through me as I sat gazing into the fire, and rolling on the rug.

'You've made my Sunday, Merlin,' he said, stretching out in his armchair after lunch, 'and I've got a present for you.' He patted the arm of his chair. 'You sit up here and we'll open it.'

Intrigued, I jumped up and sat beside him, my paws kneading the soft chair. Theo produced a paper bag with something inside. I'd forgotten the joy of crackly paper, and the special feeling of being with a human who talked to me and asked me questions, and looked at me with twinkling eyes.

Inside the bag was a brush, like the one Imelda had used on me. I sniffed it and it smelled of Josephine, so I definitely liked it.

'Would you let me brush you?'

Would I! No one had brushed me since I'd left home with Bully Boy. Being brushed was heavenly. I relaxed under the care of Theo's kindly hands as the fluff and burrs came out. He did it meticulously, stroking as well as brushing, and I loved every minute of it. I felt like a brand-new cat.

Later, when it was getting dark, I was able to repay Theo for his kindness. The phone rang and he immediately went stiff with anxiety. When he answered he sounded cold, tired. 'Hello, Theo here.' I climbed on to his lap and leaned against his heart. I listened to the voice on the other end. It sounded young, like Imelda, a woman.

'Hello, Dad. It's Sarah. Just checking you're OK.'

'Thank you, dear.'

'How are you?'

'Fine.' Theo's voice was clipped and businesslike. There was an awkward silence. Then he said, 'How are you? And . . . the boys?'

'Fine.'

'I . . . I'd like to see them, Sarah . . . and . . . and you.'

'I know you would – but we just can't come at the moment.'

Another silence. Theo seemed to be getting smaller and smaller.

'Have it your own way. You know where I live. Bye, now.' Theo put the phone down with a firm click. He huddled into his chair, beaten.

I leaned against his sad heart and purred. 'You're the best thing that ever happened to me,' he said gratefully, 'and I'd like to know how such a loving, gorgeous cat ended up as a stray.'

He showed me a photo of Sarah, in a silver frame, with two smiling little boys. 'Robin and Jack,' he said. 'They're my grandsons and I miss them. All my life, I worked and cared for my family. Now I'm an outcast, Merlin. An outcast. Sarah never forgave me for the mistakes I made – even when she knew how sorry I was. Just turned her back on me. Turned her back on her old dad. What do you think of that, Merlin?'

I thought it deserved my best plea-from-the-heart meow, so I did a really long one.

Theo was impressed. 'I do believe you can talk,' he said.

If only I could! I wished I could tell him about Imelda.

'But I'll tell you a secret, Merlin,' Theo confided. 'If I'm honest, it was my fault Sarah moved out. She didn't want anything more to do with me. I was a drunk. Every day, every night, I was on the booze, and I felt guilty but I couldn't stop. It's an illness, alcoholism, a terrible illness. It made me do all sorts of stupid things, like going to sleep in the front garden at night with the door wide open. She hated that. Anyone could have walked in, she said. Anyone! A burglar or someone who might hurt the boys. Lovely boys, they are. I miss them.' He glanced fondly at the photograph. 'But it got so bad that she couldn't trust me to be left alone with them. I was a disgrace, Merlin. A disgrace.'

He picked me up and carried me to the window. A light was flashing out over the dark sea and the moon was glinting on the waves. I could see our reflection in the glass.

'After Sarah moved out, I started going to AA meetings and following their programme. It was hard work but I made myself stick to it, and so I met some good people who helped me to sort my life out and get sober. And I love being sober. I feel like myself again, Merlin. I'm not really a bad person – but I still did those bad things. You don't think I'm bad, do you?'

I purred louder and kissed his nose. It made him smile. 'Let's not spoil our Sunday,' he said. 'I've nearly finished my miserable story. The end of it was sad. I apologised to Sarah, and I tried to make amends by offering to help her – but, no, she went all huffy, said she'd never forgive me. So that was that. I have to live with it.'

*   *   *

The following morning, I made an extraordinary discovery about Theo.

A storm was blowing in from the sea and the wind was fierce. It howled like a dog and hissed like a cat. The sea was a mass of white foam and the waves pounded the rocks with a power that made the floor tremble and the doors shudder. Theo lit the fire and the wind sucked the flames up the chimney and made it twice as hot. 'Don't you go out today, Merlin. The wind would blow you off your feet. I stay by the fire on stormy days, with my books. I love my books. Do you like books, Merlin?'

'Yes,' I meowed (a brief, high-pitched squeak).

'Let's see what we can find.' Theo stood in front of the bookshelves that covered a whole wall. 'Shall I read you a story? Or some poetry? What about *Hiawatha*? You'd like that. Or *The Owl and the Pussy Cat*.'

He chose an armful of books and spread them out on a table. I stared, astonished, at a heavy, dark green hardback with *King Arthur* in big letters, and a picture of Arthur on his horse. Imelda's book!

'Oh, you like this one, do you?' Theo said eagerly. '*Alfred Lord Tennyson's Legends of King Arthur: Idylls of the King.*'

Theo had Imelda's book. How could that have happened? Imelda would never part with it.

'Careful, now,' Theo said as I touched the top-right corner with my paw. I was careful. I knew how to open a book without tearing it. My tail twitched with excitement.

The book fell open at the page where Merlin finds the baby, where there was an illustration of the wizard. Theo froze. 'You're giving me goosebumps,' he said, round-eyed with surprise. 'How did you learn to do that?'

In reply, I put my paw on the wizard's face.

Theo's eyes opened even wider. 'Do you know who that is?'

I wanted Theo to know there was sadness and longing in my soul concerning that particular picture, so I did the plea-from-the-heart meow, followed by a loud calling meow, for I was calling Imelda. She needed to know I'd found her book, and her favourite page.

'Well, well, WELL.' Theo looked astounded. 'Have you seen this book before?'

I did the calling meow again, sending it out into the storm.

'You sound like a cat with a broken heart,' Theo said. 'Am I right? Are you grieving for someone you lost? Someone who had a book like this one?'

A silent meow confirmed it. Theo nodded as if he understood. He said no more, but picked me up and cuddled me in his wiry old arms, leaning his cheek against my head and humming a soothing tune. He carried me to the window and we watched the storm. Too numb to purr, I leaned against him and let his love heal me. He had plenty to give, and the wisdom to give it in silence.

After a while, he carried me back to where the King Arthur book still lay open at the picture of Merlin finding the baby. 'Would you like me to read this?' he asked, and sat down by the fire with me still in his arms.

I spread myself across his heart, and listened, as Merlin . . .

'Beheld, so high upon the dreary deeps
It seem'd in heaven, a ship, the shape thereof
A dragon wing'd, and all from stem to stern
Bright with a shining people on the decks,

And gone as soon as seen. And then the two
Dropt to the cove and watch'd the great sea fall,
Wave after wave, each mightier than the last,
Till last, a ninth one, gathering half the deep
And full of voices, slowly rose and plunged
Roaring, and all the wave was in a flame:
And down the wave and in the flame was borne
A naked babe, and rode to Merlin's feet,
Who stoopt and caught the babe, and cried,
  "The King!"'

The words shone like a lantern in the storm. Theo fell asleep in his chair, but I stayed alert, as the light of my angel slowly filtered down into the cottage.

'When the nine great waves return,' she said, 'all that you have lost will be restored. Be patient, Merlin, for many years will pass, and happy times they will be, for you and Theo. This is home now, Merlin. Don't go searching. Stay home, and all will be well. When the winter is over, and these rocky hillsides are covered in flowers, watch the path for a little surprise that will come your way. The dolphins will tell you. So listen. Always, always – listen.'

I basked in her radiance, and her words. I lay still, on Theo's chest, enjoying the steady, reliable beat of his heart. The angel left, lighting the raindrops on the window with the bright ruffled hem of her skirt. I saw the shimmer of her wings vanish into the storm.

* * *

Staying home was easy. I settled down with Theo. My fur became clean and lustrous again and it felt good. One day, Theo put me into a travelling basket and took me on the bus to Camelford to see the vet. I wasn't afraid. The vet checked me over and said I was a fine, healthy cat. He told Theo I was probably about one year old. 'No microchip,' he told Theo. 'Perhaps Merlin's last family couldn't afford one.' Then he gave me my 'booster' jabs, and a cuddle. His name was Tony, and I felt OK with him, and glad to be declared healthy.

There were times when Theo talked about Sarah. Growing up, she'd been a 'daddy's girl'. When she became a mum to Robin and Jack, Theo had been over the moon to have two grandsons. Then he'd lost his job and started drinking, driving Sarah away. Despite his determined efforts to become sober, she hadn't been able to forgive him. Sarah had taken the boys, and the cat, Josephine, and moved away.

In Theo's house was a secret door, which he kept locked and hidden with a curtain hanging over it. One morning, I sat by it and meowed, sensing there was something interesting behind the beautifully painted white door. I tingled with anticipation as he took down a key and unlocked it. 'I suppose you might as well see it, Merlin,' he said. 'I've kept it shut up because I couldn't bear to go in there.'

Bursting with suspense, I shot through the door and paused in surprise. It looked like another cottage with a sofa and a fireplace, a compact kitchen and stairs. It was nicely decorated but it smelled fusty and a sad, forlorn feeling hung in there, as if the place had a heart which felt unwanted.

I charged up the stairs and found two empty rooms and a bathroom. A lone teddy bear sat on a shelf in the corner, and above him was a dead pot plant covered in cobwebs.

Theo was sitting on the stairs in a cloud of gloom.

'Nice little place, isn't it?' he said. 'It was a garage and I converted it. Did all the work myself. It was for Sarah and the boys, and they lived here – for free. They moved out one terrible day, without telling me. Just upped and left. Never even gave me their new address. Not a thank you. Nothing. I've thought about it a lot, Merlin, and I understand why she did it, but I still hope she'll try to forgive me and give me another chance.'

Theo's sadness drifted like steam into forgotten corners of the abandoned home. It wasn't doing him, or me, any good. I remembered the time when my antics had made Chloe laugh. Theo was always deadly serious. I'd never heard him laugh. He kept telling me the tale about Sarah, again and again, as if it never stopped hurting him.

I wished I could tell him about Imelda, and Bully Boy.

He continued in an even gloomier tone. 'She took the cat. My Josephine. Took her away. Probably the boys wanted her. But I think I needed her more as I'm on my own.' Then his eyes sparkled again. 'But you're here with me now, you lovely cat.'

Time for a mad half hour. Instead of being saintly and purring, I'd be wild and rebellious, and clear the bad energy from this neglected home. I kinked my tail, laid my ears back and took off. I did baby lamb leaps like Bully Boy. I dragged a potato sack out of the kitchen and had the best game ever with its thick, crackly paper, its cavernous interior, and the way it slid across the polished wood floor. I fought battles with it, on my side, kicking it to death with my back legs. I dived inside, made it roll, then left it twitching in the middle of the floor. Then I pretended to be a tiger and pounced on it.

At last, I heard laughter, and Theo nearly fell off the stairs. Once he'd started, he couldn't stop. The whole place felt shaken awake and different.

'What would I do without you, Merlin?' he said finally. 'I haven't laughed like that since Josephine was here. You are a marvellous cat. I'm so lucky to have you.'

* * *

The days lengthened and the sea sparkled through the afternoons and evenings. The sun blazed down and the rocky hillsides were covered in flowers, exactly as my angel had predicted.

Theo liked to go for walks over the cliffs, or down to the cove to sit near Merlin's Cave. Sometimes I followed him, but I mostly kept away from the path because of the dogs. He worried about me getting lost, but I never did.

One day, I decided to visit Bully Boy's grave, and Archie the seagull helped me to find it. He flew ahead of me and settled on top of the rock, his legs tucked under him like a duck.

Bully Boy's grave was overgrown with wiry grasses and flowers, but the cross made from pebbles was still there. I sat in the hot sunshine, remembering him, wishing I could get him back. He was a shining cat now. His spirit wasn't in that grave, and it was lovely to see the yellow flowers growing there like tiny candle flames in the grass.

I still longed to find Imelda, and I spent time watching the many visitors who came to Tintagel. But I never saw her, and when I thought about her, I knew she was far away. Where, exactly? I didn't know. I worried about her, about how she was doing without me, but my angel had told me I was not to go searching. I must listen. It was hard to be patient.

I ran home to Theo. He was sitting outside the front door in the afternoon sun, and was pleased to see me. But I wasn't feeling cuddly. I was on edge. My fur was prickling. I knew something was going to happen. The day of the flowers. Today.

I sat up, watching the path, and I saw her coming from a long way off. A little grey-and-white cat, trotting along the path with her tail up.

Josephine was coming home!

'What are you looking at?' Theo asked, but I couldn't take my eyes off the little cat who was getting steadily nearer. Theo stood up and gave a gasp of surprise. 'I don't believe it. It can't be . . .'

I did my loud, calling meow and Josephine meowed back, and ran faster, scampering, then racing, her tail up very straight, her little face bright with joy.

My fur bushed out with excitement. I trotted along the path to meet her. I'd never stopped loving her. Just because I couldn't 'make kittens', that didn't stop me falling in love. I hoped Josephine remembered me, and she did. Her sweet face came towards me and we touched noses, both of us ecstatic. Our whiskers brushed together, and we rubbed cheeks and did purr-meows. Then we sat still on the path and gazed into each other's eyes in divine and silent love.

Theo was calling us, his voice husky with emotion. Together, we turned and trotted home, no longer lonely.

Josephine leapt into Theo's arms. I stood back respectfully but he called me. 'Come on, Merlin. Let's have you both. We're a family now!'

Reassured, I jumped on to his other shoulder, and it became a group hug, an unforgettable reunion, on the day of the flowers.

Chapter 21

'He's My Cat'

Despite Josephine's joyful arrival, it was obvious to me that she was deeply upset and exhausted. She lapped some milk Theo put down for her but she didn't want food. She wanted sleep. Her little paws were sore and she was thin. She said only one thing to me: 'I'm not going back, and if Sarah comes, I shall hide inside the sofa.'

'OK,' I said, 'I won't tell.' I knew about the hole under the sofa, a torn seam in the fabric. I'd squeezed in there once out of curiosity and found the inner world of the sofa quite roomy and comfortable. But the hole in the fabric was too tight for me and I'd frightened myself getting out. 'Why are you scared of Sarah?' I asked.

'It's not Sarah – it's the new dog I can't live with. I'll tell you later. I'm too tired now.' Josephine curled up again on the sofa. I carefully arranged myself close to her and purred her to sleep, knowing my presence would comfort her. Theo came and looked down at us. 'She's like a beautiful seashell,' he said. 'Poor little cat. I hope she didn't come all the way from Camelford on her own. We must let her sleep as much as she wants.'

Theo sat on the other side of the sofa and shut his eyes. He wasn't sleeping but praying, silently, with his hands clasped together. It was something he often did and occasionally he'd hum or sing, and I always enjoyed it. His praying created a bubble of tranquillity and hope which glowed around us. I could see it was doing Josephine good as she slept like a pearl in the heart of our love.

Through the open windows the summer twilight had begun. Theo liked to sit quietly and watch the changing colours over sea and sky. 'Better than television,' he often said. 'I don't need piped entertainment.' On warm nights, I loved to sit with him on the seat in the front garden as the stars appeared over the sea.

I will always remember the intense colours of this particular evening, on the day when Josephine had come home. For me it was a dream come true. And I remember Theo suddenly opening his eyes after his prayer, looking down at Josephine sleeping so trustingly between us.

'Everything happens for a reason,' he said, 'but we never know until we find out.'

* * *

In the morning, Josephine was brighter. She ate breakfast with me and we shared a dish without growling. 'I believe you two know each other,' Theo said. 'Have you met Josephine before, Merlin?'

'Yes,' I meowed.

'I thought so,' Theo said. 'You're all lovey-dovey.'

Josephine went straight back to sleep on the sofa. She was still there at noon when the sun blazed down on the flower-covered cliffs of Tintagel. Archie was doing laps of the house, gliding past the window where I was sitting, and peering in with his yellow eyes.

Was he trying to tell me something?

Archie flew away into the distance, then came back to perch on the gatepost. He opened his yellow beak and did his screaming, melodic cry.

My fur began to prickle. A young woman was coming up the path at a brisk walk. She looked somehow familiar and . . . she was carrying a cat basket. I stiffened. Sarah. It had to be Sarah.

Josephine was fast asleep on the sofa.

Where was Theo?

I bounded upstairs and wailed outside the bathroom. Nothing happened so I did a louder wail and scrabbled at the door.

'What's the matter?' Theo appeared, drying his face with a fluffy white towel.

Sarah's brisk footsteps were coming close, pausing at the garden gate. I sped downstairs to Josephine with Theo in my wake.

I needn't have bothered waking Josephine. The minute Sarah rang the doorbell, Josephine was instantly awake, her eyes black with fright. She moved like a flash and dived under the sofa. She must have crawled into the hole soundlessly because I didn't hear a thing. Poor Josephine.

Theo opened the front door. 'Sarah!'

'Hello, Dad.'

I jumped on to the sofa and sat in Josephine's sleeping place. I wanted her to feel my warmth above her hiding place, protecting her.

'It's . . . been a long time,' Theo said quietly. For a moment it seemed as if he couldn't take his eyes off his daughter stood at the door, her stance precariously assertive, but then he looked down at the cat basket.

'Dad, have you seen Josephine?' Sarah asked. She sounded upset. 'Is she here?'

Theo stepped back. 'You'd better come in.'

'I'm not stopping.'

'OK. Well, come in anyway. I haven't got a ball and chain handy.' Theo's eyes twinkled and the ghost of a smile passed through Sarah's face. 'This is Merlin,' he said proudly.

Sarah squatted down to see. 'He's GORGEOUS,' she breathed. 'Where did you get him from?'

'He followed me home from the fundraising evening. He seemed cold and hungry,' Theo's voice went husky, 'and he's changed my life. He was sad and lost, like me. But he's such a loving cat.'

'Aw, Dad.'

I gazed at Sarah, into her eyes, and saw a secret longing. Something I knew only too well. I had that same longing for Imelda, and for Bully Boy. But Sarah was here, WITH the person she longed for – her dad! I did the only thing I could think of doing. I reached out and put my healing paw on her shoulder.

Spontaneously, Sarah took her dad's hand and looked into his quiet face. 'Couldn't we try to be friends?'

Theo patted her hand gently. 'You're my daughter, my little girl, and I'll always love you. Not a day has gone by without me thinking of you, and praying for you.'

Words poured out of Sarah, and as they sat together I spread myself out over both of their laps. All the while, Josephine hid inside the sofa, crouching there, listening. She didn't deserve this. I made up my mind to spoil her with lots of purring and fun.

Theo listened quietly, his eyes never leaving Sarah's face, and when she'd said it all, he hugged her. 'I've made mistakes,' he said, 'bad mistakes. But I'm sober now and I enjoy my life. I want to do what I can to make it up to you, Sarah. It may be a long process, but do you think we could take the first steps? I miss you, and the boys. Everything seems precious, and beautiful, including you. Today is a new day – a chance to start again. Forgive and forget, eh?'

Sarah gave a deep sigh. 'Forgive and forget,' she said, and managed a watery smile. 'I miss you so much, Dad, and the boys do too. I wanted to put things right – so I went to Al-Anon. They help the families of . . . of alcoholics.'

Theo clasped his hands together and his eyes came alive with hope. 'Aw, yes, I know about Al-Anon,' he said. 'They've put many broken families right. I – I hope it was a good experience for you, dear.'

'Oh, it was,' Sarah said passionately. 'Cathartic – but brilliant. I wish I'd gone to them years ago. It helped me understand your illness and how I could cope with it. It gave me a map out of the heartbreak.'

Theo sat there nodding and smiling. 'Well, I'm sober now, and hope to stay sober – and be myself again.'

'We've all learned from it,' Sarah said, 'and I didn't know how powerful forgiveness can be. Forgiving you has made ME feel a whole lot better.'

'You can move back if you'd like to,' Theo said. 'The little annexe is still there.'

'Thanks, that's kind of you. We're settled in Camelford now, Dad. The boys are happy in school and I've got a job in the supermarket. But we'll come to visit you, often – and you can come to lunch like you used to.'

'I'd love that,' Theo said. 'And it's good to hear you've found a place you like. I'm proud of you.'

They sat peacefully for a while. Then Sarah said, 'I actually came here to get Josephine – but I'm glad I've got my old dad back.'

Theo smiled. 'Everything happens for a reason.'

'I knew you'd say that.' Sarah's tone was lighter and the touch of her hands on my fur was pleasant. 'So, is Josephine here?'

'She was,' Theo said, 'but I don't know where she is now. She arrived yesterday. She's OK, but very tired – and Merlin absolutely loves her. So what happened? Did she just run off?'

277

'The boys wanted a dog,' Sarah said, 'and we've got a very boisterous puppy. He's not aggressive but he's too much for Josephine. He knocks her over when he's playing, which is most of the time, and she never has any peace.'

'Well, she found her way here from Camelford,' Theo said, 'and we love her, don't we, Merlin?'

I meowed up at Sarah. She seemed to understand cat language for she said, 'You can have her back, Dad, if you like. I'll miss her but now you're sober and able to look after her she'll be happier here.'

Theo's eyes went misty. 'I'd love to have her. Let her stay. And you'll come sometimes, won't you? And bring the boys?'

'I will, Dad.' Sarah sounded relieved. 'I'd like to try to be a family again.'

'Thanks, dear, it means a lot,' Theo said, 'and of course I'll take care of Josephine.'

And Josephine came out from under the sofa.

*　*　*

I suppose grief never really goes away, no matter how happy we are. My peaceful life with Theo became supercharged with the presence of Josephine. I was happy and settled. The 'call of the wild' no longer

haunted me, and I rarely felt rebellious. And yet . . .
I still loved Imelda, wherever she was. She had been
my reason for leaving the shining lands and becoming
an earth cat. I wanted to know what had happened
to her. Was she OK now? Her words still rang in
my soul: *'You're my only friend, Merlin.'* I asked my
angel about her, many times, and she always patiently
repeated her words, 'Wait . . . and all will be restored.
Wait, and listen'.

I missed Bully Boy, but in a different way. He had
been like a guardian and mentor to me, and I still went
to his grave to remember him. One day, the man who
had dug his grave walked by and saw me in the garden
with Theo and Josephine. He made a fuss of me and
then told Theo how he had found me sitting by Bully
Boy's body.

'I reckon the cat he was with – the dead cat – was
feral,' he said. 'He had bitten-down ears and his fur was
mangy. But he was huge – black with a little snippet of
white on top of his head, and one white-tipped paw.'

Theo listened attentively, and afterwards he was
extra kind and spent time talking to me. He left the
King Arthur book out because he knew I liked to sit
on it. When summer had passed and the dark evenings
came, we spent time reading it again and looking at
the pictures. Josephine sat up on Theo's shoulder, her

eyes dilated with excitement when he was reading. We both loved to hear Theo sing. There was one line in a song he often sang which stuck in my mind, describing the passing of time:

Summer and winter, and springtime and harvest.

And years passed in Tintagel, too. There were storms with huge waves, wild skies, then flowers again, this time masses of primroses and daffodils. Then sea pinks and golden evenings.

And nothing changed.

Until, one morning, Theo took the cat basket out of the cupboard. 'Come on, Merlin. I'm taking you to the vet. On the bus.' I wasn't exactly pleased but I trusted Theo, and we'd been there before. So I co-operated. I was a sensible, mature cat now, and I couldn't even remember how to do those loud, emotive meows. I sat up nicely in the basket as Theo carried me to the bus stop.

I didn't feel spooked until we were waiting for the bus and I heard the dolphins close to the shore, singing and splashing. I knew they had come to tell us of impending change. Theo couldn't hear them. I fidgeted in the basket, trying to hold their song in my memory.

'We'll soon be there, Merlin,' Theo said as the bus whisked us inland away from the dolphins, 'and it's only a couple of jabs you've got to have. Josephine's had hers and now it's your turn.'

The vet, Tony, put his head round the door as we sat in the waiting room. 'Bring him in, Theo,' he said. 'I'll get my new assistant to examine him first. Then I'll come and do the jabs.'

'Right.' Theo carried my basket down a corridor and into the shiny clean surgery.

And then it happened. I heard a voice. I smelled a scent. My heart leapt with joy.

A girl opened my cage and gasped with surprise. A girl with solemn brown eyes. I stared back and stepped out of the cage.

'MERLIN!' she breathed.

It was Imelda. My Imelda. It really was her.

I didn't waste any time. I did a whole repertoire of purr-meows. I wrapped my soft paws around her neck and loved her, and purred, and licked her face, kissed her nose about twenty times. I was in her arms again where I belonged, and I wasn't going to leave her.

Imelda cried quietly and rested her cheek against my fur. 'I've found you,' she whispered. 'I've FOUND you.' She looked up at Theo. 'He's my cat. I know he is. I'd know him anywhere,' she said passionately.

I hung on to Imelda. But Theo was bewildered. I looked from one to the other. I loved them both. In that

281

emotionally charged moment, I realised there should be two of me. One for Theo, and one for Imelda.

How could I ever choose?

Theo intervened with his lovely calm voice. 'Take a breath,' he said to Imelda. 'We can decide what to do for the best.'

'But Merlin is my cat.'

'I believe you.' Theo's quiet words reassured Imelda. She did take a breath. 'Is this your first job, dear?' he asked kindly.

Imelda nodded. 'Yes. It's an apprentice scheme. I was lucky to get it.'

'Then . . . try to compose yourself before your boss walks in,' Theo said. 'It's obvious Merlin loves you. He was a stray when I found him, and he's very, very dear to me.'

I expected Imelda to make a big fuss, the way she used to do. But she didn't. I noticed she'd grown taller and more like a woman. Instead of 'kicking off', she took some deep breaths and calmed herself down while I patted her face with my healing paw. She seemed to like Theo. 'Where do you live?' she asked.

'In Tintagel.'

'I'm in a B & B in Camelford until I find a place I can afford to rent,' she said, 'and don't worry, Theo, I can't have a cat at the moment. I need to be sure I've got a secure home. But . . . maybe . . . I could come and visit you and spend time with Merlin? I'll tell you all about him – I had him as a kitten.'

Theo looked at her thoughtfully. 'Yes. That's a good idea – a very good idea. Come tomorrow, if you like. It's Saturday.' He handed her an address card. 'What's your name?'

'Imelda.'

'Well, Imelda, will you come tomorrow?'

'I'd love to. Thank you.' Imelda put me down on the table and looked into my eyes the way she used to do, with her hands on each side of me, her slim fingers buried in my fur. 'Merlin, listen to me. After your jabs you've got to go home with Theo, and in the morning I'll come to Tintagel and see you. OK, darling?'

I did a silent meow. Why had she put me down while I was loving her? She was sending me home with Theo. It was bittersweet. To be reunited and immediately torn apart again. I went cold all over. Tony came in and I let him give me my injections, but I felt numb and unresponsive.

It hurt even more when Imelda put me in the cat basket and locked it. Giddy with grief, I stared out at her in silence. 'I wish I could come with you now, but I can't,' she said. 'I promise I'll come tomorrow, and I'll bring you a present.'

Past caring, I sat in the basket, staring at nothing, and Theo became brisk and businesslike, marching me back to the bus stop. Bully Boy had taught me how to live wild away from humans who expected cats to conform to their lifestyles. Thoughts of escaping wormed their way into my mind as the bus rumbled back to Tintagel. I could live in a hay barn.

I felt so gutted that when Theo let me out of the cat basket, I crawled under the sofa, wanting to be left alone in the dusty darkness. Even Josephine couldn't coax me out, and she tried. Theo lay full length on the floor and peered in at me, his eyes full of concern. 'What's the matter with you?' he kept asking, but I had no way of telling him.

At bedtime, I was still under the sofa, and Josephine stayed with me instead of going to bed with Theo. I wanted to tell her about Imelda but the problem was too overwhelming. All I managed to convey to her was my burning need to run away.

Theo had never shut me in. I was free to go out into the night. The impossible dilemma pounded in my mind. Theo, or Imelda? Theo, or Imelda? Or running away.

'But what about me?' Josephine asked, her eyes big and luminous under the dark sofa.

I was going to say she could come with me. *No*, I thought. I wouldn't put Josephine through the ordeal of living wild. She was precious to me.

'Is it really what you want?' Her eyes questioned my soul. 'Do you really want to live out in the cold, and be lonely?'

Did I?

'No,' I said.

Josephine gave me a kiss. It was nice, but I still didn't know what to do.

Chapter 22

The Secret Door

In the morning, I sat on Archie's gatepost, watching the path, and when I saw Imelda coming, my anxiety vanished into the blue salt air of sea and sky. I flew to meet her with my tail up, my golden fur light as thistledown, and everything was healed by the joy of seeing her.

'Merlin!' She held out her arms, smiling and crying as we spun together in a cocoon of love. It was even better than before. She wasn't going to put me down. We were alone on the rocky hillside.

Imelda sat on a rock and listened to my purring, her cheek resting on my head. She whispered stuff to me but I was too blissed out to think about words. I just soaked up the essence of them. When we were both brimming over with happiness, she carried me along to Theo's place. Archie flew up from the roof, calling and gliding, doing laps of the cottage.

Theo was pleased to see us. He'd made coffee and biscuits and we sat in the lounge as he and Imelda talked. Josephine was interested in Imelda, and sat close to her on the arm of the chair. Theo leaned forward in his chair, hands clasped, listening intently as Imelda told the story of my kittenhood, and showed him photos of me on her mobile phone.

'Who is the big black cat?' he asked.

'Oh, that's Bully Boy. He's a feral cat. Everyone hated him, but I loved him,' Imelda said. 'He let me touch him once, and I felt so honoured.'

I peered closely at the photo of Bully Boy on the phone. He looked so small, like a beetle, but I could see it was him – the frowny eyes and the tiny pip of white on his head. I did my plea-from-the-heart meow. I wanted to tell Imelda how the big cat had brought me to Tintagel. I wanted her to know he'd gone, over the rainbow bridge.

Theo did it for me. He told her about the man who had dug the grave. 'They were together, here in Tintagel,' he said, 'and they must have been living wild. Merlin was in quite a state. His fur was a mess – and he seemed desperate and . . . broken-hearted. It took him a long time to heal.'

'I'm glad you found him, Theo,' Imelda said. 'You've obviously looked after him, and he loves you.

I'm glad. But of course I'm sad too, because I'd love to have him again, but I can't. Even when I find a room to rent, I probably wouldn't be allowed to have a cat, and he'd be left alone all day when I'm at work.'

Theo nodded. 'How old did you say you are?'

'Eighteen.'

'And you want to be a vet, you said.'

'Yes. But I can't afford to go to uni so I took this apprentice job to be a vet's assistant, and it was where I wanted to be – near Tintagel.'

'So where is your family, Imelda, if you don't mind me asking?'

'In Somerset, near Taunton. That's where I grew up,' Imelda said, 'but when I was fifteen, I had a bad accident. I got knocked off my bike and spent months in hospital, having surgery on my smashed-up leg.' She patted her left leg and rolled up her jeans to show some long white scars on her shin and around her ankle. 'It's almost back to how it was now,' she said. 'Just a bit achy sometimes if I do too much walking.'

'You poor girl,' Theo said in concern.

'Well, you could say that.' Surprisingly, Imelda smiled. 'But it was actually a life-changing experience for me. I was a lonely kid, bullied at school, and stuff. But during that time in hospital, I had so much kindness and love from the nurses and physios – and there were kids in there with injuries much worse than mine. We were all in the same boat, and we made friends. It gradually made me feel worth something, and showed me the best side of people.'

I listened attentively. Friends! Imelda had friends, at last.

'You have been through a lot,' Theo said. 'What about your parents? They must be so proud of you.'

Imelda was silent for a minute. Then she said, 'Well, Mum was proud of me. But she died of cancer just after my accident. Dad couldn't pay the mortgage so he sold our house and moved into a tiny little flat. I didn't want to live with him, but Sandie, our neighbour, said I could stay with her – and that was perfect. Sandie turned out to be an awesome friend. I could go back anytime, if I needed to. The only sadness was missing Mum, and missing Merlin. I'm so, SO happy to have found him, and glad he's got such a nice home here with you, Theo.'

Theo smiled. 'He's an extraordinary cat.'

'It's like all of my dreams coming true at once,' Imelda added, and her eyes shone with happiness. 'Merlin ran off with Bully Boy – they were buddies – and they came to Tintagel! I wonder if they were searching for me? I brought Merlin here on holiday once, you know.'

Theo still studied Imelda with kindly concern. 'You've had a lot to cope with,' he said. 'A lot. And you're doing really well, aren't you?'

'Thanks,' Imelda said.

There was a pause. Then Theo stood up. He went to the secret door, pulled the curtain aside, and unlocked it. 'Come and see, Imelda. I'm going to let this little annexe. It might just suit you – and you'd be close to Merlin. It could be the perfect solution for all of us.'

* * *

Imelda moved into the annexe a few days later with her pink-and-grey backpack and a suitcase on wheels. Brad turned up with a van full of stuff from our old home, including Imelda's bed, the rugs from the hall, Chloe's table and Granny's embroidered cushion which, he said, was for me. Josephine and I claimed it straight away and curled up together for a sleep.

Theo fitted another cat flap in the secret door so that I had access to Imelda's new home. On the first night, I couldn't believe my luck. To sleep on the softest of pillows next to Imelda was bliss, for both of us. I didn't want to abandon Theo but Josephine wanted to sleep with him, and we soon settled into our new routine.

It took me a while to get used to Imelda going to work. Was she going away for ever? Theo was kind and patiently explained it to me, every morning, with lots of cuddles and purring time, and I soon realised Imelda would come back. I took to sitting on Archie's gatepost at teatime, watching the path for her to come home, and she always did. Each day, it was like the first time all over again. I raced to meet her with my tail up, and her eyes lit up with happiness. Sometimes Josephine joined in and Theo would laugh to see Imelda come home with a cat on each shoulder. 'It does my heart good,' he'd say.

My fur shone. My eyes were bright. I could have burst with happiness.

I was a ginger cat. A nice ginger cat.

I was a ginger cat with a perfect life.

Well, almost . . .

Until, one day, the nine great waves came again to Merlin's Cave.

Chapter 23

The Nine Waves

'Come with me, Merlin.' Imelda's eyes gleamed with excitement. 'I'll carry you.' She picked me up and I settled on her shoulder.

'You be careful now, Imelda,' Theo called from the window. 'It's a spring tide today and a powerful swell coming in. Keep away from the waves.'

'Don't worry, we'll be fine,' Imelda assured him. She waved goodbye to him, and Josephine popped up to sit on the windowsill and make a fuss of Theo.

I leaned against Imelda's dark, flowing hair, and purred in her ear as she set off along the coastal path towards the cove. Being carried high above the ground was exhilarating in the fresh sea air. Today it fizzed with energy and sparkles, and the afternoon sun warmed my fur. A big swell was rolling in from the Atlantic. The waves towered and boomed, heaving up from the deep, each crest flashing green as it curled and became a speeding mass of foam.

'I want to be close to Merlin's Cave today,' Imelda confided, and I listened attentively. It was her story-book voice. Something was going to happen, like turning a page and finding magic. My fur already felt alive and electric, fluffed out like thistledown, ready to blow away on the breeze.

On the way to the cove, Imelda kept stopping to gaze at the sea. I did a purr-meow to encourage her to talk, for I sensed a stream of thoughts she wanted to share. I peeped round to look into her eyes. They were sparkling. 'I'm glad you're with me, Merlin,' she said. 'I can tell you things I could never tell a human being.' She took a deep breath. 'I've always dreamed that one day I might see the ship of light, and count the nine great waves.'

I did a yes-meow and purred in her ear. Then she said something so nice to me. She said it quietly, like a secret, with her face close to mine. 'Thank you for being my cat, Merlin. You've helped me so much, the way you've always listened and purred and let me stroke your lovely thick fur. You never gave up on me, did you? And you came all the way to Tintagel to find me – you, and Bully Boy.'

We fell silent, both remembering the dear old scruffy cat who had been my best friend.

'It's a shame he died,' Imelda said. 'In a way, he helped me too. That day when you fell in the pond and he looked after you. It taught me how, sometimes, a bully can be kind.'

Her words gave me a golden feeling of confidence and contentment. I'd come here to help her and apparently I had succeeded. Imelda walked on and again I sat high on her shoulder, glowing with happiness.

When we reached the cove, the sea was ablaze with the brassy light of late afternoon. The tide was out and a flock of seagulls stood on wet sand, their beaks to the wind. I wondered if Archie was one of them but, no – he sat alone on a rock, peering at us with his yellow eye, as if he too thought that something was going to happen.

Imelda stiffened. 'Look at THAT!' she gasped, and stared at the bright horizon where the silhouette of a cloud was rimmed in gold as it billowed across the sun. It was small and far away. Imelda quivered with excitement. 'It's like the ship,' she whispered. 'The ship of light, Merlin. It is. It really is.'

Spellbound, we watched the ghostly galleon against the diamond ocean until the sunlight mellowed, and the ship disappeared into the mass of cloud in the western sky.

'It's a symbol,' Imelda said, 'like an echo of history. A promise that the nine great waves will come again.'

Even as she spoke, a loud boom came from the ocean. The earth trembled with its power. We were at the top of the cove with Merlin's Cave on the far side. The approaching waves were enormous, the roar of surf thrum-thrumming like a heartbeat.

'I'm going to count them.' Imelda began to whisper numbers, her feet fidgeting with the unfolding drama. The mountainous waves were a long way apart, slow and majestic. 'There ARE nine! And the ninth one is gigantic.'

I could feel the excitement building, and a sense of magic made my ginger fur bush out. I remembered the legend and the pictures in the King Arthur book, of how the ninth wave had brought the baby king to the feet of Merlin the wizard. What might it bring this time? I sat up straight, my whiskers twitched and the tip of my tail flicked to and fro, brushing the blue denim of Imelda's coat.

The voice of the sea deepened as the ninth wave towered. Imelda cried out in awe as the wall of water toppled and crashed, its white foam roaring across the sand. The gulls rose up screeching and left the beach, flying far away into the western sky.

After the ninth wave, there was an expectant silence. The water shimmered, suddenly calm as if it might never break another wave.

We waited in the peachy light, but nothing happened.

'It's over,' Imelda said in her normal voice, with only a hint of disappointment. 'We'd better go home.'

But it wasn't over. I knew that. My whiskers stiffened as I listened to an extraordinary sound which only a sensitive cat like me could hear.

'What's the matter, Merlin?' Imelda held me firmly but I squirmed out of her arms and jumped down. I sat listening, my eyes fixed on the mouth of Merlin's Cave.

It wasn't a human. It wasn't a bird. What was it?

Compelled to find out, I trotted forward.

'Merlin! Don't run off, please,' Imelda called. 'We've got to go home. The tide will turn soon.'

I hesitated. With one paw in the air, I looked back at her and meowed. I wanted her to follow me. I ran back and stared into her eyes. Before she could pick me up, I did a seriously persuasive meow and set off again. She followed and I led her towards the cave. The sea was still quiet and we paused again to listen. Obviously Imelda could now hear the plaintive cry coming from the cave. 'You clever cat!' She crouched down next to me, her eyes startled.

The waves were building again but the moment of calm had allowed us to hear the persistent, high-pitched cry. 'What is it?' Imelda whispered. I didn't know. Yet the sound had a particular intonation which touched a memory deep in my heart. It was a voice I'd heard before – but this time, it was a cry for help.

My tail went up by itself, and I bounded over the stones, with Imelda, red-faced, clambering after me.

The cave floor was wet from where the tide had surged through earlier in the day. It ponged of seaweed and the light was gloomy. I soon located the sound, high up on a shelf of rock, too high for me. I stretched up with my front paws on the smooth, sea-washed wall, too steep and slippery for a cat to climb. Frustrated, I looked round at Imelda.

'It's up there,' she whispered.

'Yes,' I meowed.

'I'll find it.' She balanced on a ledge with her feet between fronds of seaweed, scanning the dark crack in the rocky wall. Then she cried out. 'A box! Some-one's deliberately dumped it up here . . . with . . . with some poor unwanted creature inside – oh, how cruel, Merlin. How cruel.' Tears dripped from her cheeks, and she took hold of the sealed cardboard box and stepped down, cradling it, already speaking soothing words to the imprisoned creature. 'I've got you, don't worry – we'll take care of you.'

I couldn't wait to see who was inside that box. I ran beside Imelda, doing purr-meows. She carried it up the beach and put it down on a cushion of turf.

The creature inside had gone quiet. 'It must be terrified.' Imelda picked at the strip of plastic tape, her face flushed with compassion. Her hands trembled but she stayed calm. She lifted the corner of the tape, peeled it off and opened the lid.

My whiskers twitched. I crept gingerly towards the box and we both peered inside.

A bright little face looked up at us.

'A kitten!' Imelda exclaimed, and more tears ran down her face. 'Who could have left a baby kitten alone in a sealed box?' She lifted him out and he wasn't afraid. He clung to her, his delicate claws hooked into her jacket. Then, unbelievably, he began to purr, and it was the loudest purr I'd ever heard, especially from such a young kitten.

'You poor darling,' Imelda murmured, carefully checking him over. His black fur was sleek and he looked healthy. He was confident, and pleased to see us. Tentatively, I stretched my head towards him and, to my delight, he responded by giving me a sweet little kiss. I noticed a tiny pip of white on the top of his head and he had one white-tipped paw.

Why was he staring at me so boldly with his baby blue eyes? He seemed to know me – and he loved me! Suddenly I knew. I knew him.

I blinked. Imelda's smile confirmed what I was thinking. It was HIM. It was really, really him!

If cats could cry, I would have wept tears of joy.

Bully Boy was BACK. Born again as a tiny, perfect kitten.

'It's a miracle,' Imelda said quietly. 'Come on, Merlin – help me love him. He needs you as well as me.'

She had the kitten on her lap. I crept up there and wrapped myself around him, and we purred together with Imelda gently stroking his little head with one finger. The air was chilly now and shadows of the evening coloured the sea and sky.

'We'll take you home.' Imelda stood up and tucked the kitten inside her coat, close to her heart. I lay on her shoulder, gazing down at him, and already he was falling asleep, still purring. 'You'll be safe with us, little one,' Imelda said, 'and in this lifetime, you won't be a wild cat alone in the cold. You'll have a forever home with us and we'll always love you – won't we, Merlin?' I reached down with a soft golden paw and put it close to the sleeping kitten so that he'd know I was there.

'And,' Imelda added, 'this time, we'll call you by your true name – Beautiful Boy, or "BB" for short.'

The evening star shone over the sea as we headed home with a sense of deep contentment and joy.

Imelda glanced at me fondly. 'I love you, Merlin,' she said. 'Thank you for being my cat. You've helped me so much.'

I responded with a purr-meow. I was glad to have helped Imelda, and she had helped me. My fur was glossy and well brushed. My eyes were bright, and I felt majestic.

I was a ginger cat. A happy ginger cat.

ACKNOWLEDGEMENTS

I would like to thank everyone who helped me to create Merlin's story: Beth Emanuel for her meticulous typing; my agent, Judith Murdoch, for believing in me; my editor, Tara Loder, for the love and care she has put into making this lovely book. And gratitude to the friends who have given me so much encouragement and support: Carolyn, Pam and Audrey, and our wonderful Writers' Circle.

ABOUT THE AUTHOR

Bestselling author **Sheila Jeffries** has been writing since she was young, and published four novels before she left school. After studying at Bath Academy of Art, Sheila spent many happy years teaching in UK schools, and as a successful artist and writer. Her latest book sees her return to the world of her bestselling novel *Solomon's Tale*, which though it was fiction, was based on two real cats that shared and enriched her life. Sheila lives in Somerset where she enjoys teaching meditation and running workshops for writers.

WELBECK

PUBLISHING GROUP

Love books? Join the club.

Sign up and choose your preferred genres to receive
tailored news, deals, extracts, author interviews and
more about your next favourite read.

From heart-racing thrillers to award-winning historical
fiction, through to must-read music tomes, beautiful
picture books and delightful gift ideas, Welbeck is
proud to publish titles that suit every taste.

bit.ly/welbeckpublishing